CAPTAIN BLOSSOM SOLDIERS ON
or Run Away, Someone's Coming

by the same author

KNOCK OR RING
A ROOM IN CHELSEA SQUARE
WHEN THE BED BROKE
BLANKET (by Henry Stratton)
CAPTAIN BLOSSOM

Captain Blossom Soldiers On
or Run Away, Someone's Coming

MICHAEL NELSON

Leo Cooper London

First published in Great Britain 1974 *by*
LEO COOPER LTD
196 Shaftesbury Avenue, London WC2H 8JL
Copyright ©*1974 by Michael Nelson*

ISBN 0 85052 178 5

Text set in 10/12 pt. Monotype Baskerville, printed by letterpress, and bound in Great Britain at The Pitman Press, Bath

FOR FRANK PIKE

Foreword

After the war in Italy had been brought to a successful conclusion with no help from me, I had to remain in the army a further year until I was demobilized.

Regrettably the events of this year had faded from my mind, so I took myself off to what my old drivers of the Royal Army Service Corps would have called a Trick Cyclist, upon whose couch these further memoirs were conceived. It was a painful progress, for as we trod together the shameful path of my military career, further acts of cowardice, incompetence, immorality and negligence were dredged up from my subconscious. Although what we mostly discovered were some of the crimes I committed in Italy after the war, we also brought to the surface several incidents that occured during the final months of hostilities, which my sub-conscious had done its best to repress.

In all fairness I must warn members of the Band of Hope that this is not the book for them. There is a great deal about alcohol and its effects in its pages, because this is the way it was.

Reviewing Captain Blossom one critic wrote at the end of his piece: 'Is it possible that Michael Nelson could have been such a drunken craven coward?'

The answer is yes.

On enquiries I discovered that this particular critic served in one of the posh regiments. I think it was the Brigade. For the benefit of those lucky ones who escaped or were too young to suffer the terrors and indignities of life in His Majesty's forces in wartime, the Brigade means the Brigade of Guards. The Guards are so grand that they are unable to think of any other Brigade existing except their own. This supreme confidence in their superiority, their inability to address anyone with civility save the Sovereign, one another, and God, in that order, makes them the finest soldiers in the world.

Members of the Brigade, together with almost everybody else in the Army, Navy and Air Force are pretty rude about the Royal Army Service Corps. I think only the Pioneers are lower down the social scale, and the Ordnance and the Royal Electrical and Mechanical Engineers rate about the same. I know one young man, whose father was an ambassador, who is so ashamed of having been a ranker in the Service Corps, and a clerk, not even a driver, at that, who when questioned about his service states that he was a Trooper, and leaves it to the person who had the audacity to ask such a leading question to decide for himself in what kind of an outfit he trooped.

The Royal Army Service Corps was undoubtedly overloaded during the last war. It contained more men than any other arm of the service. But they could not possibly all have been dishonourable men. It should not be mocked, if only because within its ample bosom the Corps offered refuge and some measure of safety to persons like myself. After all the war would have been won no sooner had men like me been shot for cowardice. Nothing would have been gained and valuable ammunition would have been wasted.

I am increasingly grateful to the Corps for having nursed me through those unpleasant years, and am not in the least ashamed to answer when asked what I did in Hitler's War: 'I was a Driver in the Royal Army Service Corps, 260166, Sir.'

When as a reporter in the late '50's I joined the Good Ship Associated-Rediffusion Television, under the command of the late Captain Tom Brownrigg R.N., the first thing that I noticed was that the doors of the offices in the building were plastered with names and ranks, all followed by the letters R.N. There was Captain This R.N. and Lieutenant-Commander That R.N. sprouting like mushrooms in every corridor and on every floor. So proud was I of my association with the dear old Corps that I had inscribed on a plate and fixed to my door the words DRIVER NELSON ROYAL ARMY SERVICE CORPS.

Much has been told of the fabulous Captain Tom Brownrigg R.N. before his retirement from Associated Rediffusion and his untimely death. I would like to put on record for a wider public my favourite story concerning him.

There was a senior technical appointment to be made. Captain X, an old friend of Captain Brownrigg, came to him and said: 'Tom, I propose to appoint so-and-so.'

Tom Brownrigg considered the proposal and shook his head: 'Can't have the fellow.'

'But he's got all the technical qualifications, he's just the man for the job.'

'Can't have him,' said Tom Brownrigg. 'The fellow's a bugger.'

Captain X considered this piece of information for a minute.

'I was not aware that homosexuality precluded one from employment in the company, Tom,' he said.

'That may be so,' answered Captain Brownrigg, 'but not in the engineering department!'

Chapter 1

Soon after I was commissioned I was posted to a company responsible for supplying a division with what was left of the petrol which had not leaked out of the flimsy cans or been flogged to the petrol-starved civilians by avaricious drivers. Here I was put in command of a platoon.

One of my N.C.O.s was a certain Sergeant I must call Smith, and I apologize to all Sergeants of like name, but in view of my own shortcomings I have no desire to expose this particular Sergeant to ridicule.

Sergeant Smith was a splendid Sergeant. Over six feet tall, he could have served in the Brigade and made a fine soldier. His drill was impeccable, well up to Brigade standard. My only criticism was that when he entered my concrete-floored Nissen hut he would throw up a perfect salute and crash his foot down with a noise like a clap of thunder which would shatter my brain, already beginning to suffer from the primary effects of whisky, into fragments. His voice matched his boot. It would echo across miles, commanding some idle driver to remove his hands from his pockets and march in an orderly and soldierly manner. His eyes were the eyes of a hawk. A matchstick at a hundred yards distance, a speck of dirt on the underside of a blancoed belt, never once escaped them.

I don't think my drivers went in fear of Sergeant Smith. They laughed at him; called him the biggest bullshitter of all time. At the same time they had a healthy respect for his strong sense of discipline and his knowledge of King's Regulations. As far as I was concerned it was a godsend to have such a sergeant. It gave me an opportunity to ease myself quietly into the life of the platoon, without having to give orders which I might later regret. So I left the day-to-day running of the organization to Sergeant Smith, put my feet up on the stove in my Nissen hut, and read Proust right through for the first time.

My second Sergeant, Sergeant James, was a very different type of soldier; quiet, reserved and endowed with a measure of cool authority which obtained for him immediate obedience without the necessity of adding to the noise that emanated from Sergeant Smith. On the few occasions when I emerged from the seclusion of my hut to make a round of inspection with both of them, I did not fail to detect a glimmer of humour in Sergeant James's eyes as he watched Sergeant Smith up to his antics, whether bawling out some unfortunate soldier or apologizing to me in rapid barks for the inadequacies of the scum under my command.

'Don't worry, Sir. Couple of days. Lick 'em. Lick 'em, Sir. Last thing I'll do, Sir. Couple of days, Sir. Won't recognize the idlers. Idlers, Sir. Idlers Sir. They are, Sir. IDLERS, SIR.'

I would await with apprehension the end of the performance.

Sure enough, on the last 'Sir' which would reach a crescendo and almost knock me off my balance, up would come that right foot, and down it would go with all the weight of Sergeant Smith's fourteen stone of muscle behind it.

Thanks to Sergeant Smith my drivers were eventually lured onto a train, battened below hatches on board ship, and carted in conditions that cattle would not have been endured, to that cesspit of the world called the Middle East.

Together with these unfortunate men went loads of equipment, mostly useless, to be discarded in the sands of the deserts, or pilfered by the Wogs and sold to God knows whom in the various bazaars, a bazaar being a place where two wogs or more were gathered together to trade in stolen property. I don't think in those days that anything was sold legitimately in the Middle East.

The responsibility for drawing up the lists of our platoon equipment was in the able hands of Sergeant James, and quietly but efficiently every one of my men was equipped with everything from his Housewife to his obsolete rifle. The latter each man had taken with him to a nearby range and fired off five rounds of live ammunition, very few of which came anywhere near the target.

Sergeant James went up further in my estimation when without shouting or threat of courts martial, he managed to lumber certain drivers, admittedly of lower intelligence than the rest, with the heavy pieces of hardware, among which was the infamous Boys anti-tank rifle. The Field Kitchen equipment was so heavy that I think it must have been manufactured to be carted about by a different breed of men from ourselves. So cumbersome was it that it secured for its exclusive use one three ton lorry. I never ceased to admire my jolly Corporal Cook Venner and his two assistants for the unfailing cheerfulness with which they humped this gear on and off that lorry without doing themselves serious injury.

So with Sergeant James' quiet efficiency and Sergeant Smith's bawling and threats of immediate execution in the field, which he assured me was permissible in time of war and the one thing in his life that he would love to see more than anything else carried out, my platoon and I wandered about the Middle East like one of the lost tribes of Israel for several months, without, it is hardly necessary to add, doing anything to further the defeat of the enemy.

After much planning, heavy expenditure of ammunition and loss of life, Montgomery ousted the Germans and the Italians from the Middle East and I couldn't help wondering at the time what had induced them to try their luck in such an unhealthy climate. But I was not impressed by the standard of Generalship on either side.

Now was to come our finest hour. My platoon, together, with the rest of the company commanded by Major Hawkins, set about training to invade the mainland of Europe. There was talk of that soft underbelly by the old Warrior Churchill. I was aware that the Dardanelles disaster of the Kaiser's war was not his fault, or at least so he kept telling everybody, but was due to the lackadaisical execution of the project by the commanders on the spot. Nevertheless I secretly prayed that we would not be landed on the inhospitable coast of Salonika or be asked to slog our way through the mountain ranges of the Balkans. I asked God not to allow us to be put ashore on the Southern tip of Italy or Sicily and ordered to drive our way to Berlin, having to cross mountain after mountain, penetrate gorge after gorge, in a campaign that could only be compared to those ancient skirmishes on the North-West Frontier, the difference being that the campaigns of the North-West Frontier were waged against Fuzzy Wuzzies, who while admittedly committing appalling atrocities on one's manhood should one be unfortunate enough to fall into their hands, could in no way be said to command the modern methods of destruction as did the Germans and the Italians. Not that the former considered the latter anything but natural cowards who had to be carried all the way, usually backwards.

In preparation for the invasion of an unknown piece of coastline we waterproofed our vehicles, drove them in and out of the Bitter Lake, more often leaving them in than out.

Major Hawkins' sense of destiny waxed day by day. Constant inspections ensured that all our equipment was in a state of immediate and offensive use. In Major Hawkins' mind lurked the dangerous conviction that a Company of the Royal Army Service Corps was a fighting machine as efficient and aggressive, even more so, than a company of infantry. Try as I did to disabuse him of this idea, I failed. All I succeeded in doing was in confirming his growing belief that I was idle, slovenly, lacking in moral fibre, with an increasing addiction to the bottle no matter what it might contain, and far from being suitable officer material. As a result of this correct piece of deduction, Major Hawkins kept a special watch on me and my platoon, with the result

3

that at my request Sergeant Smith redoubled his energies and ensured that every man in the platoon looked the part, whatever each might feel individually. At the same time Sergeant James saw to it that every piece of equipment was cleaned, oiled, rubbed and polished, to protect it from the ravages of the sand, flies, and general effluvia of the Middle East. Guards were doubled against the thieving local population, who circled the acres of barbed wire that surrounded the camp, but it proved of little use in repulsing their forays into our midst to bear away some piece of equipment, of seemingly little benefit to them, but which would appear the following day in the local bazaar together with other ironmongery that had once belonged to the British Eighth Army.

One bright day Major Hawkins called his officers together and imparted to us the alarming information that our Brigade was to spearhead the invasion of a place of which he had cognizance, but the name of which for security reasons, could not be trusted to officers below field rank. He ordered us to pass this information on to our respective platoons, and like Nelson he told us that he was confident that each one of us would do his duty. As he made this reference to Nelson, he stared in my direction.

It was after I had informed my platoon of the bad news that, looking back, I can see now that Sergeant Smith's personality began to alter. It is easy to be clever after the event, but I can clearly recollect that when the time came for him to dismiss that memorable parade, there was a distinct lessening of the decibels in his words of command.

I have never seen anyone go into a sudden decline from consumption or other wasting disease but that's what happened to Sergeant Smith, from the time of that parade, at an ever accelerating rate. Within two days his voice had sunk to a whisper. The crash of his boot into the sand as he threw up his salutes no longer raised a duststorm. His guardsman's upright posture began to lurch forward as if his spine had collapsed.

It seemed to us all at the time that it was as if some malignant growth within was eating the man away before our eyes. It had to be an inward disease, because outwardly Sergeant Smith did not alter. He still looked his fourteen stone; his face was brown and it was reported to me by Corporal Venner that there was no diminishing of Sergeant Smith's vast appetite and that he still paid frequent visits to the cookhouse to devour a tin or two of bully beef wedged between the issue biscuits which were impervious to destruction save by the toughest molars. These snacks, so Corporal Venner informed me, were still washed down with five or six cups of tea and several tablespoons of sugar.

I was mystified by this information, because all my own illnesses had been accompanied by a loss of appetite. It occured to me that perhaps it was my duty to take the initiative and instruct Sergeant Smith to report sick. On second thoughts I decided that Sergeant Smith might reproach me for suggesting that now that the hour had come for us to do our duty to King, Country and the Empire, that he should absent himself from the glory that awaited us.

I should not have worried. A few days later Sergeant Smith came to my tent and asked to speak to me privately. Accordingly I asked my Lance Corporal Clerk to step outside.

'Sorry to bother you, Sir. May I have your permission to go sick?'

'Of course, Sergeant. You know there's no need to ask me. All you have to do is to report to the MO tomorrow morning.'

'Thank you very much, Sir.'

'That's all right, Sergeant. I've noticed you've been off colour the last few days. I hope it's nothing serious.'

'So do I, Sir,' said Sergeant Smith. 'But I'm very worried, Sir. Very worried. I'm prepared for the worst.'

'I'm sorry about that, Sergeant,' I said, not wishing to probe into Sergeant Smith's mysterious illness.

There was no need for me to probe.

'It could be serious, Sir. It runs in the family I'm afraid.'

'What runs in the family?'

'Ulcers, Sir.'

I gasped aloud. Nobody could look less like suffering from ulcers than Sergeant Smith.

He held his hands across his stomach. 'It's like a knife, Sir. Like a knife being twisted in my guts.'

'You should have gone sick sooner, Sergeant,' I said.

Sergeant Smith looked contrite. 'Truth of the matter is, Sir, that I knew I was sick before we left England. Perhaps it was wrong of me not to report sick then. But I felt I couldn't let you and the platoon down, Sir. They might have said I was trying to dodge the column.'

After I had dismissed Sergeant Smith I went in search of Sergeant James to whom I divulged the startling news of Sergeant Smith's stomach ulcers.

Sergeant James looked me straight in the face 'If this bloody shower of ours is having to go into action and face the enemy it's not a bad thing if we shed the sick, the maimed and the dying before the shit starts to fly.'

I left Sergeant James, turning over his words in my mind. I am ashamed to say a nasty suspicion had started to rear its head.

Major Hawkins was disbelieving when I went to his Headquarters and told him that I looked like being one Sergeant short when the time came for me to disembark my men on a hostile shore.

'Damned awkward. Still, I can let you have my headquarters Sergeant. Once we're at grips with the enemy, he can lay off the bumf. Won't do him any harm to have some experience in the field.'

The following day Sergeant Smith departed to a hospital in Cairo to have his insides X-rayed.

Three days later he returned. As I saw him alight from his fifteen hundred weight truck, and come striding across the desert towards me, I could see by his upright and soldierly bearing that all was well. On the way he paused to bawl out an unfortunate driver on guard duty who was chatting with a fellow driver instead of being on the alert and ready to repel any attack by the wogs.

Across the desert air his voice rang true, all the glory of its former decibels restored, as he threatened Field Court Martial and execution on the spot to another unfortunate driver discovered smoking at the wheel of his wagon.

Finally he halted in front of me and, before I could beseech him to refrain, had brought his foot down on the desert enveloping us both in a cloud of sand.

'Permission to speak, Sir?' he thundered.

'Speak on, Sergeant' I said bemusedly, wiping the muck from my eyes. 'Glad to have you back looking so well.'

'Bad news, Sir.'

'Bad news?' I said unable to hide my surprise.

'Very bad news, Sir,' he roared, still standing rigidly to attention.

'Stand at ease, Sergeant.'

I immediately regretted this act of kindness on my part. Sergeant Smith executed an acrobatic feat of which he alone was capable. Both feet left the ground and landed at the same time on the sand, once again showering me in a cloud of dust.

'Bad news. Incipient ulcers, Sir.'

I must have looked incredulous for he added: 'Medics insist treat 'em now before they develop, Sir.'

'Well, we'll have to look after you, won't we, Sergeant?'

'No, Sir. 'Fraid not, Sir. More bad news, Sir. Regret very much shall be unable to remain with you, Sir. Greatest blow in all my service, Sir. Great blow, Sir. Just my luck it should happen at a time like this. Tried to talk 'em out of it, Sir. Wouldn't listen to me. Did my best, Sir. I would give my right arm not to have let you down, Sir, at this time. My right arm, Sir.'

6

I declined this offer of a piece of Sergeant Smith and instructed him to report to the Company Sergeant Major.

'What will happen to you?' I finally asked.

Sergeant Smith tapped his battledress pocket. 'Instructions here to report in three weeks time for medical regrading. Thought of tearing 'em up, Sir. At a time like this knew my duty was with you and the men.'

'Why didn't you, Sergeant?'

'Gave it a deal of thought, Sir. But you wouldn't thank me would you, Sir, if I went sick on you when you and the men were in action against the Hun? You'd never forgive me, would you, Sir?'

Three weeks later we set out in convoy for Alexandria to take part in what was to be the invasion of Sicily.

The last I saw of Sergeant Smith was on a motor cycle as he roared up and down the column shouting his best wishes mixed with exhortations for us to show the enemy that the boys of the R.A.S.C. meant business.

When he passed me at the head of my platoon he performed the seemingly impossible by sitting upright on his motorcycle, with both hands down the seams of his battle dress trousers, throwing me an eyes right, followed by an impeccable salute the like of which you would not see on the square of Wellington Barracks. Mustering all the power of his voice to overcome the roar of the platoon three tonners he shouted: 'Good luck, Sir. Good luck, Sir.'

I have never seen him since.

That evening, after we had parked our transport in the neighbourhood of the docks, I sought out Sergeant James. My nagging suspicion had been worrying me. Had I in my secret thoughts been maligning Sergeant Smith? I put it to Sergeant James straight. I didn't wrap it up.

'Do you think Sergeant Smith deserted in the face of the enemy?'

'Of course,' replied Sergeant James quietly. 'We had a bet on it in the Sergeant's Mess before we left England. You see, we all knew about this incipient ulcer. Headquarters Sergeant had seen it on his Medical card. We were all of the opinion that in the unlikely event of this mob being called upon to do some active service, he would reactivate his ulcer. In fact we held a sweepstake as to the exact month he would decide to go sick.'

'You don't seem very upset about it.'

'No, Sir. I held the winning ticket.'

Six weeks later my platoon, its water-proofed three tonners, our equipment and ourselves, all by now somewhat depreciated by the efforts of the thieving Wogs were still waiting to embark. By that time

Sicily had been cleared of the last German and Italian, and the allied armies had moved on to the Italian mainland.

I have reported on Sergeant Smith's ulcer to illustrate the truth of the army belief that 'the bigger the bullshitter, the more useless the soldier'. Lest it be said that I have held him up to ridicule to take the spotlight off some of my own shameful conduct, I propose to follow immediately with some stories of my personal shortcomings.

As far back in my childhood as I can remember I have always been a natural coward. I was afraid of the dark, of thunder, of lightning, of cows, dogs, spiders, mice and rats. At my first school I was bullied unmercifully, and called a cry-baby. I never once fought back. To this day if I detect violence in the air, I immediately change location. No one, not even my dearest friends, can count on me to come to their aid in the event of their getting involved in a fight. Film director Pat Ward has affirmed publicly that in the event of violence breaking out in a public house where Michael Nelson is drinking, if he can't get out of the door, you will discover him lying flat on his face under the nearest table with his hands pressed to his ears. It's all very well for Pat Ward to tell the truth; he's six foot six, strong, healthy and younger than I am.

Up to the time of the crossing of the River Garigliano I had only come under some desultory shell fire. I did not like it one little bit, and it always amazed me how the infantry and other branches of the army who had to live for several weeks at the sharp end were able to stand their ground. It was easier for me, because I was only subjected to these showers of high explosive for a limited amount of time, that's to say when delivering ammunition to the guns, taking troops towards the front line or handing over food or petrol. These activities sometimes called down what was known as a stonk, in which some keen members of the opposing party would point an '88 roughly in the direction in which they could hear the grinding of my drivers' gears and loose off some high velocity shells. But as these operations were nearly always carried out after dark their shells always went wide of their mark.

The real dangers of these night operations were the roads and mountain tracks that had to be negotiated with no lights. I think it was here that the phrase was coined about keeping death off the roads. Sometimes the leading vehicle would come to a sudden halt as one of its front wheels edged off the road above a thousand foot drop. Immediately the trucks behind would concertina into one another. My batman, Driver Lane, did his best but he was a poor driver in the daylight, let alone in the dark. On one occasion I got out of my fifteen hundred weight to lead him along a goat track, whereupon he ran me down and I was pinned under

8

the vehicle for the best part of an hour, while my drivers gathered round me in the darkness and debated how to extract me without doing me permanent damage.

These night escapades were complicated by the fact that we were operating in a god-forsaken country which, in winter-time, turned into one great morass, and not once in the Italian Campaign were we issued with four-wheel-drive vehicles. I suppose the pre-war planners had imagined that we should be taking supplies up the Great West Road.

It is true there were Jeeps around, particularly towards the end of the campaign. These were in plentiful supply in the base areas where every officer could be seen tootling around with these delightful toys. On paper I was entitled to one but I never received it, so I soldiered and slithered on with my fifteen hundredweight truck.

In the crossing of the Garigliano I was allotted a highly important role. About a dozen of these useless fifteen hundredweights were put under my command, driven by drivers from the infantry battalions. Why this was I cannot recollect unless a wave of sickness had suddenly swept through the ranks of my platoon.

For the benefit of non-military readers I should explain that the crossing of the Garigliano was another of those disastrous exercises that distinguished the Italian Campaign. Theoretically the river would be crossed by two divisions on the West Coast, while a landing at what turned out to be Anzio would be made behind the enemy lines. The two would join up and the enemy, attacked inland as well, would pull back in full retreat.

It did not work that way for two reasons. The German Commander, Kesselring, didn't want to retreat, and it is claimed that there was too much caution on the beaches of Anzio on the part of the Allied Commander on the spot. This may be so, but in view of Kesselring's natural aggression it is arguable that if the forces landed on the Anzio beaches had pressed on to Rome they would have been extremely thin on the ground. There is no reason to suppose that Kesselring would have decided to withhold his counterattack, and these thin Allied Forces might easily have been cut to ribbons.

The crossing of the Garigliano proved no more successful. There was one reason for this, namely the inability of the allied command to realize that Southern Italy is a country of high mountains. The enemy must have viewed our crossing with amazement as they squatted in their mountain fortress, shelled the pontoons and ferries that we tried to throw across the river, and pinned down those troops unlucky enough to have made the crossing and reached the foothills.

To supply these unfortunates crouching behind their rocky sangars with ammunition and food was not easy and required all the resources of the supply section of the divison. To play a small part in this was the reason for my being placed in command of those fifteen hundredweights.

A few hours after the crossing, loaded with food and ammunition, including, to my horror, a great number of mines which were to be laid in preparation for German counter attacks, I made my way towards the one and only remaining pontoon, the other having been successfully destroyed during the course of the day by German '88s and mortars. The knowledge that we were within mortar range had produced in me a sensation of utter terror.

For some reason Driver Lane was not with me and I was being driven by a battle-scarred and hardened infanteer from a Scottish Regiment.

In the back of my vehicle were cases and cases of rum. This I knew was the only place that this precious load could be carried if any of it was to reach the fighting troops who so desperately needed it beyond the river. Jock and I broached a case and stowed away a bottle apiece.

Much to my disappointment the rum did not have the hoped-for effect on my morale. If anything it sank lower.

We reached the pontoon without mishap, and apart from the odd shell or two which landed too near for my liking, causing me to plunge headlong into the shelter of the mud, we managed to manhandle the fifteen hundredweights on to the pontoon bridge and finally we all landed without mishap on the other side. Here we were to be met by guides who would lead individual vehicles to where they were required. But as is always the case with military guides, they are never there to do the guiding.

This set me a problem. What was I to do with my fifteen hundred-weight trucks and their valuable contents? My first reaction was to return immediately across the pontoon to the comparative safety of the south bank. I discarded this thought as the enemy started to put down a heavy barrage on that fragile structure. So I pressed northwards for about half a mile until, finding myself in a deep lane, I halted and called a conference. By now I was almost completely incoherent. It seemed to me that I had entered Dante's Inferno. On all sides were burning farm-houses, while here and there dumps of petrol and ammunition exploded, lighting the entire landscape.

To the front, loud and clear, came the rat-tat-tat of brens and the answering call of the German burp guns. Rifle shots pinged overhead. To my right a heavy spate of mortaring was making life extremely un-comfortable for some poor wretches, while overhead cascades of our twenty-five pounder shells whined on their way to the Germans entrenched and laughing in their mountain fortress.

Eventually one of my drivers discovered a very tired infantry subaltern who, instead of being grateful to see us with our loads of good cheer, was distinctly hostile, particularly when I mentioned the mines and promised that my drivers would unload them with no inconvenience to himself. I even threw in the additional bait that I would not ask him to sign for them.

'For Christ's sake get to hell out of here. There's enough shit flying about without you and your idiotic circus bringing more down on us.'

'Let's unload the junk here and get to hell out of it, Sir.' said Jock. 'Don't pay any attention to the officer. He's in a right state.'

In the light of a new conflagration which had suddenly appeared a couple of hundred yards away as a result of some judicious mortaring, I could see that my drivers, who were now crouching round me waiting for my decision, did not even want to waste time putting Jock's suggestion to the vote.

I was about to give the command to unload and to proceed individually and with all haste back across the river when, with a deafening bang, something landed at the rear of my convoy.

I dived into the mud as rocks and stones and more mud showered down on us. I lay for several minutes sobbing loudly, until I felt a hand touching me on the shoulder.

'It's all right, Sir. Nothing to worry about, Sir.' I heard a voice say.

I slowly raised myself from the arms of mother earth and saw Jock standing looking at me and shaking his head.

I felt no shame. It never occured to me that I should have behaved otherwise. All the careful preparation to make me a leader and an example to my men had gone by the board. I was shown in my true light, a gibbering, useless coward.

I found myself incapable of getting to my feet. Instead I squatted on the ground, ready to hide in the mud at the next explosion.

'First time, is it, Sir?'

'Yes.'

'It's always bad the first time, Sir. You get used to it after a bit. Get to know the buggers that are dangerous and the ones that are safe. Of course the one that's got your name on it you never know about.'

At that moment I heard one that I could have sworn had got my name on it approaching and I returned to the sanctuary of the mud.

When I emerged I could see that Jock had gone back to the vehicle and started to unload the rum.

I went to help him. He held out a bottle: 'That's what you need, Sir. I don't think you've had enough. If I may suggest it, Sir, you'd better get really pissed. Kind of paralytic, Sir, and with any luck you won't feel a thing.'

I took his advice. I woke up twelve hours later in what seemed strange surroundings, until I realized that I was in the back of a fifteen hundred-weight covered with blankets. At my side was a crate of rum and an empty bottle. I crawled out of the truck to discover that I was in my own platoon lines, south of that hateful river.

Sergeant James saw me, came over and said: 'Had a good sleep, Sir? Hear you ran into a bit of trouble last night. Your Jock driver said you behaved splendidly and retrieved a dicey situation.'

'He what?'

'Of course he was pissed, and so I gather were you. Incidentally, Major Hawkins wants a report on the operation back at Headquarters. He's been sending dispatch riders every half hour asking where you are.'

'What did you tell him?'

'Said you were still across the river making sure that the last of your men had come back safely.'

'Where's Jock?'

'Been called back to his battalion. Apparently they've had such a mauling they're down to one company strength and need every man they can lay hands on.'

'Did he say anything else, Sergeant?'

'No. Oh yes, he asked me to wish you the best of luck and looks forward to seeing you in Sauchiehall Street.'

God bless you, Jock, wherever you are.

Funnily enough, Jock was right. The first time was decidedly the worst. After a bit one came to tell the difference between ours and theirs. Later on one could detect the near-misses which necessitated one assuming the horizontal position. But I would not like to give the impression that I ever became familiar with shells. They always scared the pants off me.

I mentioned just now some of the things that frightened me as a child, but I forgot to mention that a particular object that terrified me was a German helmet that my father had bought back from France where he had served with the Gunners in the Kaiser's war. This horrible object was perched on the end of a German rifle and stood in the corner next to his desk.

One does not have to be particularly well-versed in Freudian theories to realize that this placed me at a decided disadvantage when the time came for me to oppose the second desecration of Europe by the un-speakable Germans.

Shortly after the catastrophe of the Garigliano our division was pulled back and sent to reinforce the second catastrophe at Anzio. This was far too near the enemy for my liking. Indeed I even watched them through my field glasses walking about wearing those terrifying helmets, which reduced me to a state of gibbering fear.

Captain John Fish, my very good friend, was aware that I was not cut out for the military life, let alone military glory, and very kindly allowed me to spend most of my time on the Anzio bridgehead holed up several yards underground with bottles and bottles of rum for compan-ionship, while he looked after the day-to-day running of the platoon, exposing himself to shells and shit with an alarming disregard for his personal safety. After his day's or night's work was over, and he had ensured the safety and comfort of his drivers as far as was within his power, he would join me in my haven and inform me of the events of the day. Throwing cares aside we would discuss our lives and loves, and what we would accomplish in the days of peace if ever they should come.

The Anzio beachhead began to reel under the lash of Kesselring's counter-attacks and the pounding of his '88s. So serious did the situation become that some drivers of the Royal Army Service Corps were called upon to do service in the lines.

One evening a terrifying code word, something like Backpassage, was delivered to our dug out. This meant our last hour was at hand, that the Germans would attack all along the front, and at the same time send in a taskforce by sea to attack us from the rear. As we were encamped in a pine wood bordering the sea, this put our platoon in great jeopardy, and me into a state of mounting terror.

Leaving me to my thoughts and the bottle, John went fearlessly out into the night, doubled the guards, established bren posts, and every-thing that he had learned at O.C.T.U., thus ensuring that should the Hun land he would encounter at least one island of resistance.

That night not even the rum could bring me sleep. I lay in a stupor listening to the roar of the guns. Both sides were firing at the same time, and whoever had sent out the codeword was right in supposing that an attack was coming in from the front. The question that plagued me was whether a second attack would come in from the rear.

During the night, at regular intervals, John would rise from his camp bed, don his equipment, pick up his Tommy gun, climb the steps of the dugout and make a round of inspection to ensure that the drivers were alert at their posts.

At about three in the morning John had just returned from a tour of inspection when all hell was let loose. A burst of bren gun fire, mixed with rifle and the clatter of a Tommy gun, broke out overhead, literally within spitting distance of the dugout.

I turned my face to the earth wall and prayed to God that my end should be swift and there should be no wounding and no painful lingering. John was out of the dugout before I had finished my prayer.

I lay in the darkness listening to my own breathing. Outside there was silence, although towards the front the guns still thundered. I don't know how long I lay in that darkness, my heart palpitating, palms sweating, bowels about to burst open. Maybe only a few minutes, maybe an hour. Still silence. I could see those Hun helmets swarming across the drivers' positions. Perhaps they were an enemy commando and were quietly dispatching the wretched drivers with their knives.

Still no sign of John. I could bear it no longer. Forcing myself to my feet, I struggled into my equipment, weeping quietly to myself. On my right hung my Colt '38. I drew it out, not quite knowing why, possibly subconsciously thinking it would be better to finish it then and there by putting it to my head and blowing out my brains.

In a pouch attached to my equipment lay two black Mills bombs. Shaking with fear I took one out, with great difficulty inserted the primer, and made my way giddily towards the foot of the stairs that led upwards from the dugout.

To my horror, as I stood at the bottom of the stairs, I heard voices. Then came a footstep. Someone was coming down. Any moment the German grenade must land at my feet. I knew from every book about the business that you always tossed a grenade into an enemy dugout before paying a personal visit. The steps grew louder. I drew my pistol and holding it with both hands pointed it towards the bottom of the stairs. I don't know what my motive was. It certainly wasn't my intention to take one Hun with me. I was about to squeeze the trigger when I heard someone say: 'Trust those bloody drivers to loose off at one another, the silly sods.'

I dropped the pistol on to the ground. I have never seen John so frightened. 'Christ Almighty, you might have killed me, you silly sod,' he shouted.

By the tone in his voice I knew he was really angry with me.

It is a golden rule in the Army that one should never volunteer for anything, on the principle that, however attractive the proposition might look, there is sure to be a catch in it somewhere. I concurred with this widely held opinion until the winter of 1944.

It was bitterly cold that winter, once again confirming my suspicions that the travel agents who painted a picture of sunny Italy in winter were nothing but a band of lying rogues.

The war had come to a stalemate in a line that ran roughly from the plains round Ravenna in the East to the mountainous country round Bologna to the West. In this desolate area of snow and ice, the two weary armies faced one another and tried to keep as quiet as their generals would allow them. Even the generals by this time had sensed the tiredness of their men, and had given up ordering that 'aggressive patrolling' should take place.

I had more or less retired into a shell, sharing a hovel with some villainous members of the Field Security Police. Owing to their powers of arrest and imprisonment of the civilian population without trial, they lacked nothing. Gifts of wine, brandy, fresh bread and meat, arrived in a steady flow, and on festive occasions a supply of young girls.

Unfortunately news reached Headquarters that I was falling down on my job, which was true in the most literal sense. Accordingly I found myself driven out by my Commanding Officer to take a more active part in the war. I was forced to accompany my drivers as they delivered ammunition to the guns, or carried one load of troops into the line and another out.

One day when I had reported to Headquarters to receive my orders for the day, the second-in-command, quite a pleasant Captain, who nevertheless was fully aware of my incompetence and was moving heaven and hell to get me posted to another mob, asked me if by any chance I could ski.

I told him that I could.

'You can ski, you really can?' he said incredulously.

'I may be a drunk but I'm not a liar,' I said pompously.

Rubbing his hands together he said, 'In that case I shall foward your name to Army H.Q. They're calling for volunteers to form a ski battalion.'

'Exactly,' I said. 'They're calling for volunteers, and on no account will I volunteer.'

'Have you no sense of duty?' the second-in-command said petulantly.

'None whatever,' I replied, saluted and made my way back to my platoon.

At eight o'clock the next morning I was back at Headquarters.

'What is it now?' asked the second-in-command.

Drawing myself to my full height I said: 'I wish to volunteer for the ski battalion.'

'You what?'

'With one reservation. I have made enquiries and would like you to confirm that it is a two month's course.'

'I have the papers here,' he said looking down at them. 'It is thought that the formation and training of the ski battalion to a high degree of fighting efficiency will occupy at least two months.'

'You may forward my name.'

He looked at me suspiciously. 'You're not suffering from some form of mental aberration?'

'My sense of duty returned overnight,' I replied.

Ten days later I received orders to report to a former peace-time skiing resort in the mountains fifty miles north of Rome.

It is incredible to think that although the campaign in Italy was being fought in the winter amoung mountains deep in snow, no one in command had up to this time, as far as I could discover, thought of forming a ski battalion to oppose the ski troops the enemy had in action.

It's possible, of course, that the generals may have thought that the Italians, ninety per cent of whom had deserted the Germans and come over to our side, should have fulfilled this vital role. After all their Alpine troops were said to be among the best in the world. I think this should read among the best in Italy, which is like saying rotten mackerel doesn't smell as bad as decayed herring.

Anyway, at this peace time resort north of Rome were gathered the nucleus of the new ski battalion, some two hundred officers and men from all branches of the army, from the infantry, from the gunners, from the Service Corps and even a couple of A.C. Plonks from the Royal Air Force.

In command there was a splendid Colonel decorated with the Polar medal, which it was said he had received for peering through a hole in the ice for one whole Arctic winter. There was nothing he didn't know about survival in Arctic conditions, and he was like a friendly schoolmaster willing at all times to join in the games with the boys. He was, in my opinion, just the kind of officer under whom it was a pleasure to serve. Strange as it may seem, he was even able to rekindle within my twisted mind some measure of enthusiasm for the task that lay ahead. I never though of him as a colonel, which was one of my criticisms of so many officers in the Royal Army Service Corps. They were wildly over-conscious of their rank.

Beneath the Colonel were several officers and other ranks chosen as members of the Directing Staff for their peace time abilities. Among their numbers were champion skiers, famous mountaineers, medics who had been on peace-time expeditions to the Pole, and even a handful of people who indulged in that dangerous pastime, bobsleighing.

We were housed in four grand and well-heated hotels, waited on hand and foot by hordes of white jacketed Italian servants. I could hardly believe my good luck, although I was shocked to discover that the bars, which were open twenty four hours a day, were lacking in gin, whisky and brandy. This was on the orders of the Colonel. But there were plentiful supplies of excellent wines.

Within a few days we were issued with splendid equipment. Specially manufactured American mountain warfare clothing was thrown at us with a liberality that I had never before experienced in the army. Nothing was too good for us. As the Colonel frequently admonished us, we were the cream of the cream; we were superior to the Guards and the Marine Commandos.

The only thing we were not issued with were offensive weapons. We had a few light American carbines, which we took to bits in the classrooms, and of whose theoretical use we obtained a sound working knowledge. Some mountain howitzers were promised, and we studied these on the drawing board, memorizing each nut, bolt and pin.

I had never been so enthusiastic. For the first time in my military career I was happy. My companions were delightful, whether officers or men. I had never before served in a unit like it. There was no rank, no class, no backbiting. I suppose the truth was that each one of us regarded each day as a holiday, the whole experience as an unexpected windfall. We could not believe our good luck.

Mornings and early afternoons were devoted to skiing, walking, and elementary climbing.

I had learned to ski in Switzerland in 1938 during a winter holiday chiefly memorable for my first love affair. I often wonder about the girl. She went by the remarkable name of Cherry Sue Orr. I wrote her the most beautiful poems, and the first time I kissed her was on New Year's night in a cellar filled with boys and girls all in some form of clinch. I remember with what sadness I said farewell to her a week later, as she departed for Grenoble University. I bombarded her with more poems and ream upon ream of heart rending love letters. She answered. Our letters grew shorter. Postcards followed. Then silence. *Sic transit.*

Now as I skiied each day, something of the happiness of those days of my adolescence returned to me. I felt less depressed. My health improved. The grog blossoms on my ravaged face seemed to fade away as did the signs of a premature corpulence which was beginning to show at the age of twenty-two.

Apart from the skiing I particularly liked the long treks through the mountains in patrols of nine or ten men, each man taking it in turn to lead and set his own pace. From these training patrols I actually learned something which I was to take back to civilian life. When going uphill, never hurry. Go at a snail's pace, taking short steps. On no account try to race up a hill. A slow crawl will get you there quicker in the end and in far better nick.

Some of my companions were not so happy about climbing but I was lucky. I had spent most of my childhood in South Devon, and was adept at scrambling about the cliffs in search of gull's eggs. Heights held no terror for me. Now for the first time I learned to climb properly, using ropes and minimizing the danger. There was no question of climbing for sport within the Queensberry rules. We banged pitons into the mountain side; we used every method available to us to get us aloft without damaging ourselves.

I must confess that I didn't care much for the nights we had to spend in our flimsy tents, dug into the snow trying to hot up biltong over a candle. In spite of the Colonel assuring me that, dug deep into the snow, one would be as warm as a bug in a rug, I could never get round to agreeing with him. I lay awake the whole night, my teeth chattering, devising ways of avoiding such uncomfortable nights.

The late afternoons and early evenings, if we were not on these extremely unpleasant night exercises, were devoted to study in the classroom. We were taught the principle of mountain warfare, although what they were I cannot remember. We perfected our skill in tying knots, from bowlines to reefs to half hitches. I found for the first time that my days in the Boy Scouts had not been in vain, and I passed out Victor Ludorum in the knot competition to the admiration of my companions and the congratulations of my instructors.

On skis I excelled too.

The ski lift was not often used, the Colonel being of the opinion that lifts were dangerous; that people carried up mountains by ski lifts always set off downhill with cold limbs. In the event of a crash, this would render them far more liable to fractured bones. He insisted that we climb upwards with skins on our skis, so that we were in fine fettle with relaxed and warmed bodies when we started our descent. Besides, he pointed out that when the time came for us to go into the mountains further north to harass the Hun, we would not have the benefit of ski lifts.

For some reason one day the ski lift was in action when I returned from a practice patrol. The Colonel was standing at the top of it, watching the men come up one by one with their bottoms propped on the hooks that hung from the overhead cables.

'Had a good day, Michael?' he asked me. 'They tell me you're doing very well. Looks to me that if you can keep it up, you could pass out of here commanding a platoon.'

To this day I can remember my pride and joy at that moment. For months and months, through my own inadequacies and bloody-mindedness, I had been kicked around, quite rightly, like an unwanted cur. Here was encouragement at last. How could I show my gratitude, and further convince this charming man that at heart I really was a leader of men, an officer of courage and initiative?

Watching the hooks of the ski lift coming up each with a man attached and the empty ones going down, I was suddenly inspired. I would show the Colonel of what I was capable when properly led and encouraged.

Without saying a word but offering a silent prayer to the Almighty, I dug my sticks in the ground and pushed off. I heard the Colonel cry out, but I ignored him.

Down the solid packed ice of the path of the ski slope I sped, swinging my body to right and left as I turned in and out of the ascending and descending hooks of the lift. I shall never forget the looks of horror and fear on the faces of the men coming up. Several fell off in surprise.

I am not a particularly good skier. It was a mad thing to do, and something that one would only do with the deliberate intention of showing off. But I won through. The Almighty heard my prayer. With a final Christiana I negotiated the last turn and, unable to stop in the space available, crashed into the side of the power house at the bottom of the lift.

As I picked myself up, I could see the Colonel hurtling down the slope. More expert than I, he came to a halt beside me in a shower of powdered ice hurled up by the steel edges of his ski.

He looked down at me and said: 'You silly fucker, Michael. Let's go up to the mess and have a drink.'

It was shortly after this episode that the Colonel announced that as we had behaved so splendidly and learnt our lessons so well we should be allowed to visit Rome and stay a night if we were not on duty. Although no actual offensive ironware had yet arrived, about this time the Quartermaster Captain received a batch of shoulder flashes on which were embossed in gold the splendid words MOUNTAIN BRIGADE. As soon as these were issued we handed them over to the Italian servants who sewed them on to our mountaineering smocks. Then we swaggered off to Rome to lord it over all the other troops on leave.

The effect of this badge had the most startling effect on members of the opposite sex. There can be no question that in wartime Rome they have never had it so good. A thousand men to each woman gave them the marvellous opportunity to pick and choose at will. And who can blame them? The result was that the plainest girl could choose the most handsome man and turn down the rest with impunity. The highest-ranking officer would be more than delighted with the company of the lowest-ranking girl.

As a mere Lieutenant in the Service Corps my rating was nil, and I had long ago given up all attempts to cultivate the company of an American or English girl. Instead I contented myself with the Italian girls, purely on a commercial basis. As I was never short of money, thanks to the activities in the Black Market of my batman, Driver Lane, I was able to secure for myself tarts of a remarkably high standard. Indeed they were not usually professionals, but amateurs reduced to the oldest profession by the exigencies of war.

I arrived in Rome with a dozen of my colleagues and we made straight for the bar of the Excelsior. Within an hour we were surrounded by a group of admiring females, whom we regaled with large drinks inter-larded with stories or our heroic battles in the mountains. Why had we not been heard of before? Because, I replied, we had been most highly classified, and this was the first time that we had been allowed out of the mountains where we had been continually at grips with the German mountain battalions.

It was on my return to the mountains that I realized to my relief that my seemingly unwise gamble in volunteering for the ski battalion had come off. We were all travelling in the back of a three ton lorry and as we came to a small village half way up the mountains we decided to stop at an albergo for a glass of wine. Outside there was snow in the narrow streets and it was still lying on the roofs of the houses. It was so warm that we asked the landlord to bring the wine outside.

As we stood gossiping, feeling very pleased with ourselves, and dis-cussing the adventures of the previous night, I was suddenly conscious of something wet on the back of my neck. I felt it a second time.

At the same moment a bird on the telegraph pole on the opposite side of the street started to sing. I looked up and saw that the snow on the roof of the inn had started to melt.

Seeing me looking upwards the landlord said: 'It's good, no? The spring he come very soon.'

By the time we had completed the course, although the offensive ironmongery had still not arrived, spring had come. The snows melted, the first mountain flowers spread their petals, on all sides nature burst into song, the ski battalion was disbanded and we were returned to our units.

Perhaps here, although it belongs in the future when the war in Italy was over, is the place to mention my second successful attempt to dodge the column by volunteering.

It occured when I had been posted to Bari to a General Transport Company commanded by a brutish ex-ranker who had been promoted Major by someone with a perverted sense of humour.

By this time a great number of lucky soldiers had been sent home to be demobbed, and this Major was furious at being ordered by Area Head-quarters to find an officer to volunteer to go on a messing course in Milan.

Being a regular he was amazed at my volunteering. I proceeded to Milan where I experienced the dubious honour of being picked up by a tart in the great cathedral.

However, I was out of the Major's bullying hands for four weeks, in addition to which I learned how to reconstitute dried egg powder, which I cannot believe was of great benefit to myself or to anyone else.

Chapter Two

I'm sensitive about my drinking problem in the same way that some homosexuals are always affirming their normality by expressing an excessive interest in girls, or accusing every man within sight of suffering from their own deviation.

Some drunks are greatly admired for their ability to put away vast quantities of liquor. 'He's a bottle a day man', or 'it's nothing for him to see off three dozen bottles of Guinness'.

But there's nothing clever in such feats. They merely put more money into the pockets of the Distillers Company and the Guinness family, who have got far more than is good for them already. I would never encourage any boy or girl to start drinking if they can do without the stuff. I go wild when I hear people say how civilized the French are because they start their children off with wine and water the day after they have come off mother's milk. No nonsense about drinking hours in France. No need to hurry or throw back drinks in a rush in France. You never see a drunk on the streets in France. Then how do you account for the fact that France has the highest incidence of alcoholism in Europe?

To encourage young people to take up alcohol, which is nothing less than a deadly drug, is criminal. I would like to see all forms of advertisements for drink banned by law. It is particularly sickening that such advertisements should try to make the young feel unsmart if they don't try to kill themselves with vodka, gin, or whisky. I can assure all young men that consumption of spirits does not improve their virility let alone their chances with a girl. Indeed, they'll find if they allow the grog to get hold of them that they'll develop that curse of the drunkard known as brewer's droop.

While we soldiered together through the Middle East and crawled our way up Italy, Captain Fish and I had many memorable booze-ups together. At the time we did not pay great attention to them, or bother to think that the damage they did to our livers was considerably more than we were inflicting on the enemy. We had no sense of guilt, and because we did not look to the future, we did not pause to consider how our gargantuan consumption would affect us in the years to come.

John is a person I am still delighted to meet. When we get together he has a special way of asking about my health. Instead of saying: 'How are you?' he asks: 'Still hitting the bottle?' If I deny it and say that I've cut it down to a mere smell of the barmaid's apron he will look at me sternly and say: 'Come off it, Michael. You're an alcoholic. We're both alcoholics.'

I don't agree with him. He gave it up for twelve years on the trot. But we do suffer from a basic failure with the stuff. Neither of us cares to muck about with it. Once we start drinking we get the bit between our teeth.

A few weeks ago I went out to dine with a novelist. I do not particularly like him because his desk is always tidy with everything in its correct place; his carpets are immaculate and if anyone drops ash on them, he brushes it up then and there with a dolly dust pan and brush. The whole house is on permanent show and absolutely uncosy. I further dislike him because of his regular output. He works from nine till one and half-past two till six, turning out reams and reams of highly readable prose. He is successful and makes a great deal of money, another reason for not caring for him.

'Will you have a glass of sherry before we dine?' he asked. I replied: 'I would hate a glass of sherry. Give me the bottle and I'll most certainly have a drink with you.'

I have not been asked to dinner since.

Over the years I have become skilled at spotting drunks. The problem of getting the drunk to the table is a sure give-away. If you notice that the man is drinking a lot before the meal and plying his guests with booze, it does not automatically mean that he is a soak, but the moment his wife begins to chivvy him towards the table, you can be sure that he is a true boozer. Alcoholics love to drink on an empty tummy—just one more, then another one before eating is their idea of heaven. Left alone they'll never get to the table but make some remark like 'Had a big meal at the office today' or 'Not hungry, my dear. What a pity. It looks so delicious.'

More marriages have broken up through drunks failing to appreciate the hours of hard work that wives have devoted to dainty dishes than through any other cause. Compared with this sin, infidelity is nothing.

During the time we were training to land on the hostile coast of Europe and I was being verbally lashed by Major Hawkins, and no doubt would have been lashed physically if it had been permitted by King's Regulations, one of those welcome breaks that sometimes befall subalterns dropped out of the blue.

My platoon was ordered to proceed south along the Suez Canal and set up camp at a place that went by the remarkable name of El Shatt. It did not belie its name It consisted of a few hovels constructed with empty petrol cans cemented together with camel dung. Here lived a handful of the most miserable human beings I have ever seen. How they managed to stay alive was beyond my comprehension. They had no food, no work, no nothing.

My attitude in those days towards them was one of revulsion and hate for the amount of trouble they caused with their thieving ways. Of course they were entitled to steal. How else could they stay alive in the unspeakable world into which they had not asked to be born? How they must have hated and envied us, who appeared to have been blessed with all the riches of the world.

John and I set up camp up-wind of El Shatt, but that proved no protection from the swarms of flies who, smelling richer pickings within our lines, deserted the native population and fell upon our men like a plague of locusts. Soon we were all suffering from Gippy Tummy, and the Canal Zone resounded with the loud protestations of our guts.

Since that period on detachment at El Shatt my insides have never been the same again. To this day if I pass over any country in the Middle East five miles up in an aeroplane, with uncanny accuracy my tummy knows we are in the danger zone, and I am stricken with a recurrence of Gippy Tummy.

John was greatly perturbed by the effect this was having on the morale of the men, so one day, having asked me gently if I was capable of taking command for a few hours, he disappeared with a three-tonner in the direction of Port Tewfik.

It must have been about dusk that I heard the sound of a honking horn and saw in the distance a three-tonner scorching across the sand in a somewhat erratic fashion.

As it came closer I saw John at the wheel. Ignoring the sentries who had the good sense to get out of his path, John drove the truck into the centre of the camp, removing half the cook house on the way, and came to a halt in a flurry of dust.

As I approached he got down from the cab, steadying himself with one hand against the door as he hit the ground.

'Where's Sergeant Smith and Sergeant James?' he demanded.

'Sir!' bellowed Sergeant Smith stamping a foot in to the sand.

'You and Sergeant James will personally with the aid of the Corporals unload this truck and store its contents in the Sergeants' Mess.'

'Sir!' thundered Sergeant Smith and I saw John wince.

'You will have the cases of gin brought to Mr Nelson's and my tent and stowed beneath our beds. You will inform the men that in return for a three-ton load of beer they will keep their hands off the gin. Understood, Sergeant?'

'Sir!'

From that day onwards life assumed a rosy hue, as John and I set about getting through a considerable number of cases of Nicolson's gin. To this day when I pass the home of this splendid gin and see its name high in the sky at the western end of Theobald's Road, in London, I still offer up a prayer to God for the peace of Mr Nicolson's soul.

It was a sad day when John and I consumed the last bottle of that memorable consignment on the airfield at Foggia in Italy. We drank it sadly inside John's caravan, for, not to be outdone by General Montgomery, John had acquired a luxury home on wheels, which he graciously allowed me to share. Although I was never invited to tea by Monty I bet John's caravan was considerably more comfortable.

I asked John, when he arrived back at El Shatt with that happy load, how he had acquired it.

'Won it at cards,' he replied.

'How do you mean, won it at cards?'

'Went to the NAAFI. Have a friend there in charge who was at O.C.T.U. with me. Charming fellow but dim. He was moaning about his lack of personal transport. He's got a bird tucked away and has to thumb lifts into Cairo to see her. So I got him on to a game of Slippery Sam, promising him my own fifteen hundred-weight if he won. He hasn't a clue. I remembered him from O.C.T.U. days giving his money away at poker. So I strung him along until I'd won enough. Instead of taking the cash, I collected my winnings in kind.'

John insisted that I get up early next morning to take first parade. I do not know if this was sadism on his part, but I can still remember being assisted into my uniform by Driver Lane, who also draped me with my various accoutrements. Forbearing a swig at the gin bottle, I staggered out into the blinding sunlight. With Sergeant Smith at my side I steered a zig-zag course along the lines of drivers on parade praying to God that there would be no driver's cap awry, no rifle incorrectly positioned, which would occasion a bellow of fury from Sergeant Smith and send me reeling to the ground.

When I had finished my inspection, I saw Captain Fish waiting on the edge of the parade for me to report to him. He always looked immaculate. His Khaki Drill reflected the morning sun, his pistol sat in its holster at a jaunty angle, and his face was the picture of good health. How dare he manage it on a bottle of Nicolson's, I mumbled to myself, as I stumbled towards him.

Slithering to a halt before Captain Fish, I made a poor attempt at stamping my feet together, nearly collapsed into the sand, and threw him up a salute that would have made any self-respecting R.S.M. have kittens on the spot.

'All present and correct. Parade ready for your inspection, Sir,' I managed to croak.

Captain Fish looked at his watch.

'Late as usual, I see.'

'You sodding bastard,' I muttered.

'You said something, Mr Nelson?' said Captain Fish leaning towards me. 'Incidentally, I think it's high time you persuaded that idle batman of yours to dress you correctly. I suppose you are aware that your lanyard is on the wrong side?'

'We're not a bloody cavalry regiment, Sir'.

'On the contrary we are entitled to wear our lanyards on the left which is an honour. Kindly conform in future.'

'Sir,' I spluttered, secretly calling Captain Fish all the filthy names I could muster under that desert sun.

After the parade had been dismissed, Captain Fish and I breakfasted in the shelter of our tent. Eggs and tinned bacon, toast and marmalade and tea were all of the highest quality. Being in a base area we were able to secure plenty of freshly baked bread. The only thing lacking was butter. The margarine supplied in its place was inedible. It tasted of axle grease and, even when placed out in the midday sun which would fry an egg, it still refused to melt. In spite of John's researches, together with those of his batman Driver Jacks and my Driver Lane, we never did manage to lay our hands on any tinned butter.

Personally I doubted whether it existed. But John swore he had seen some at General Headquarters in Cairo where he had a friend in the Supplies and Transport Department. John had friends everywhere.

John was a good officer and, I must confess, without him to keep some control over me, I must surely have fallen completely to pieces. I suspect now that he drove me out on to those ghastly morning parades to keep me off the gin bottle before breakfast.

Although John seemed to have friends in every department of the army, whether at Brigade, Division, Corps or even Army Headquarters, there was nothing of the creep about him. He had the advantage of enjoying army life, and did not fall into my error of regarding time in the army as a continual battle against those put in authority over me. Beginning with our own company he established a very good working arrangement with its commander. As a result he could get away with murder as far as Major Hawkins was concerned. If he got drunk or fell foul of the Brigadier, Major Hawkins would be the first to hurry to his defence.

John was one of those wartime soldiers who were blessed with an aura of luck. It literally radiated from him, and one felt in his company that no misfortune could ever befall one. This irritated me at times, because when I was with him I always came off second best. You could say that John always secured the favours of the pretty sister, while I was always landed with the ugly duckling.

After breakfast at El Shatt John would depart in his fifteen-hundred-weight truck to report to Headquarters and receive orders from Major Hawkins, and make a round of the locations where our drivers were working to see that all was well. At the same time he kept an ear open for information that might be of use to us. For instance he might hear a rumour in one of the NAAFI bases that a consignment of Scotch was due in at Port Said on such and such a date; that some fine American blankets were to be found at a certain Quartermaster's stores somewhere in the Canal Zone; that a truckload of Spam had arrived at such and such a railhead. Spam at that time was a scarce and highly tradeable commodity, although I much preferred the traditional bully beef on which, in the Second World War as in the First, the British Army continued to march.

I spent my mornings in the company of Sergeant Smith and Sergeant James miserably inspecting the lines, checking kits, crawling underneath vehicles on the pretence of inspecting their undersides and reporting any defects but in fact only too grateful to get out of the sun. All the time my mind was on that glass of Nicolson's that would be poured out for me at midday on the return of Captain Fish.

As midday approached my spirits would slowly gain momentum. I always looked forward to John's return, wondering what spoils he would bring with him. One day it might be a handful of fresh limes or some precious ice to be stacked away in one of the cookhouse's enormous hay boxes which required two drivers to shift. On one occasion he even secured some Russian caviare. I think this must have been filched from Headquarters Cairo, because it was around the time that some Russian politicians had been meeting there to discuss the future conduct of the war.

Probably the most remarkable occasion was when John returned for lunch bringing with him two nurses from the local hospital. I said earlier that English girls were reserved for the higher ranks, but this naturally did not apply to John. While I was grateful to him for considering my

27

basic needs I doubt whether any man would have been capable of sexual operations with the particular darling he brought back for my delectation. I disgraced myself by tipping the gin bottle frequently in my own direction, and falling asleep across the trestle table while the Bully Beef à la mode de Shatt was being served up by Drivers Lane and Jacks, both suitably attired in waiters' jackets in honour of the ladies.

John was very angry with me but, as his fury had no effect on me whatsoever, he took the line that I had been extremely ungrateful in not appreciating his efforts on my behalf, and that I had hurt him so much that in future he proposed to leave me to fend for myself. This did not fool me. Long before I fell asleep I had realized that mine had not come along for the pleasure of meeting Michael Nelson, but to protect her friend from John's advances.

The entertainment of these two nurses was a once-off because, after my appalling behaviour, John declared that he would not subject his lady-friend to a further display of bad manners on my part. In future he contented himself with wining and dining her at one of the many Officers' Clubs in the Canal Zone, and occasionally would drive with her into Ismalia and dine at the Greek Club. As a result I was able to return to my midday libations with no fear of reprimand, eat my lunch without recourse to polite conversation, and stumble onto my bed where I would immediately fall into an unhealthy slumber.

The evenings at El Shatt, after the return of the drivers to camp, were given over to sports and bathing in the Suez Canal. Sport was always football and I never ceased to be amazed at the energy the men could find for kicking a ball about, no matter what the climate. Halt a convoy in the desert or in the snow-covered mountain of Italy and two things would happen. Each section would produce a cut-down four gallon petrol can, fill it with precious petrol, set it alight, and brew up, each section competing with the other to produce the best cup of tea in the platoon. At the same time a football would appear and on the edge of a precipice or much too near a mine field for my liking some energetic practice would soon be under way.

Although I occasionally bathed in the Canal I was put off by the foreign bodies and other noxious solids that floated on and beneath the surface of its cooling waters. The Canal was very narrow at El Shatt, and I never ceased to be amazed by the sight of the ships that seemed to be moving across the sand.

Looking back on those days at El Shatt with Captain Fish, I can see now that they were among the least unpleasant in my army career.

However, there was established there a steady basis of drinking that

28

was to reach its crescendo a couple of years later in Italy. At El Shatt I was out of the range of Major Hawkins' criticism and disapproval, so it was with great regret that John and I received orders to strike camp and return to our company to continue training for the invasion of the mainland of Europe.

During the Six Day War between Israel and Egypt it was with a feeling of sorrow and nostalgia I read of the 'heavy straffing' of El Shatt by fighter bombers of the Israeli Airforce.

I sometimes think when I look back over my career in Hitler's War that I should have performed better than I did. Many of my friends are of the opinion that I failed to impress my seniors because of my drinking habits. It is arguable, and I tend to think it to be nearer the truth, that my drinking habits arose through the inability of the Higher Command to appreciate my potential. Their blindness to my natural military genius produced in me a state of mind which resulted in my taking to the bottle in disgust.

During the course of my month's residence on the Anzio bridgehead I was once ordered to take out a patrol at night. It was very dark and I was loath to commit myself to such a hazardous undertaking. There were uncharted mine fields to be skirted, nervous drivers lurking on all sides with fingers on the trigger. Indeed it was a prospect that appalled me. I cannot think what came over Major Hawkins to issue such an order.

However, I set out with Sergeant James, not having the least idea what the object of the exercise was but determined that it should on no account be an aggressive patrol. I kept Sergeant James beside me and behind us stumped a warrior of the First World War who had recently been presented with a Lance Corporal's stripe.

There were a great many flares in the sky, and I was about to suggest to Sergeant James that it would be wise for us to hide up in a ditch for an hour or two before returning to report 'no enemy activity encountered and patrol returned safely to base', when a particularly bright flare exploded overhead. I was first to the ground, and looking round behind me saw this Lance Corporal with his arms outstretched and still standing motionless upright.

'Get down, you bloody fool' I whispered.

'No, no, Sir. If you freeze like this the enemy will mistake you for a tree.'

A few minutes later the flare burned itself out and we resumed our wanderings. It wasn't till I had gone round in a circle that something suddenly dawned on me. My only companions were now Sergeant James and the Lance Corporal.

I attribute this to bad thinking on my part. From that day on I realized that an army must be led from the rear as well as the front.

Naturally in the course of the conflict in Italy I gave considerable thought to the question of bravery, and regarded it with admiration under any circumstances. I even admire bravery when the person isn't aware of his heroism, being either ignorant or drunk.

I tend to be rude about the fighting qualities of Americans, but I can remember well during the critical days at Anzio when the bridgehead seemed certain to collapse, watching the American Fortresses flying over some two hundred strong in tight formation. There was no avoiding the ackack barrage that waited for them and they flew straight into it without faltering. Every day some ten would explode in midair. This was true bravery. These fliers took their chance and did not turn back, knowing that nothing could prevent the loss of a certain percentage of the attacking force.

I have always been impressed by what I call 'upper class' bravery, a kind of nonchalant attitude towards death and danger which is the prerogative of upper class Englishmen who with a strange mixture of arrogance and sheer stupidity believe that no harm can ever befall them. Of such arrogance are Empires made, and when there is no longer much of it about, Empires tend to fade away.

I was taking a Guard's battalion into the line. They were to pass through a battalion already there, and attack a mountain that reared up bang in front of the line.

The Major commanding the company that was to spearhead this attack was a good friend of mine. Looking back I think he was amused by my inability to conceal my dislike for the noise and the danger. I must confess his calmness and his disregard for the hostile surroundings while discoursed on the merits of fishing on the Test as opposed to the Itchen did do something to quieten my fears.

Indeed I was so emboldened by his behaviour that I agreed to proceed on foot with him after he and his company had disembarked from my trucks to what was ironically referred to as the start line.

This line was the bed of a deep mountain stream. Here we crouched while our artillery put down a barrage in the mistaken belief that it would make the attack easier for the infantry.

Languidly the Major looked at his watch, remarking, 'Here we go, chaps. The time has come for us to attack the common enemy.'

Without a glance in my direction he stood up and, armed only with a shepherd's crook, started to walk towards the mountain that housed the Germans. He had walked for fifty yards before his head was blown off by a mortar shell.

I have been asked if I ever performed a brave act. I think if one means by that question did I ever feel like running away and forced myself to stay, the answer is yes.

It must have been shortly before the invasion of Sicily when our company received a consignment of incendiary grenades. These, when dropped to the floor, exploded in a sheet of flame that would burn anyone to death within a ten to twelve yard radius. Major Hawkins, determined to bring my drivers to a peak of fighting efficiency, gave orders that I should instruct them in the use and delivery of these obnoxious grenades.

In spite of my outward reassurances that the grenade was as safe as a baby's rattle, in spite of my digging a deep trench and throwing up a protective wall in front of it, over which this dreadful missile would be hurled, I could not but be alarmed by the shaking hands of some of the drivers.

As I remember one pulled out the pin and then had ten seconds in which to get rid of it or be burned to death.

Twenty drivers successfully launched a grenade over the parapet where it duly exploded.

It was that same Lance Corporal who had instructed me at Anzio to freeze and look like a tree who was nearly my undoing.

I handed him a grenade, he removed the pin, and crouched down *still holding it*.

'Get rid of it, you bloody fool' I yelled.

'No, no, Sir. Can't have Jerry tossing it back at us' he replied coolly. 'Five, six, seven, eight . . .'

I threw myself to the ground. With a roar it exploded just over the protection of the parapet, scorching the back of my head.

I looked up.

'Well I'll be damned' said the Lance Corporal, 'it's burned off my eyebrows, the little bugger.'

Chapter Three

I was serving with Major Thompson's company which serviced an armoured brigade, and was passing through Ferrara with my trucks loaded with ammunition for the tanks which at last were racing to the north, when the Italian Campaign drew to its victorious conclusion.

As a result of a somewhat wild night on the part of my drivers and the effects of the grappa which they manufactured in their portable still, we were a little late taking the road the following morning.

The entire Allied Army was on the road, led by its officers in pursuit of loot, the most prized being some form of enemy transport. Mercedes were highly favoured by officers of Field rank. At the bottom of the scale you might see a Captain driving a Volkswagen, and Lieutenants had to content themselves with the odd motorcycle combination.

As we made our slow way along the main road passing thousands and thousands of dejected prisoners sitting by the roadside I could not help being amazed at the skill with which the Enemy Generals had managed to keep their army in Italy supplied in spite of the complete mastery of the skies by the allies. I suddenly realized, that behind their front line troops who were very well equipped, there was hardly any mechanized transport. The equivalent of my mob, and the other R.A.S.C. companies that operated even further back from the sharp end than we did, relied on horses and mules.

The prisoners watched us without any signs of emotion as we edged our way forward. The Germans did not ask us for anything. They were content to squat and watch us. They were not even guarded. It was clear that they had no intention of escaping. After all, where could they go? If they went through Austria they would probably fall into the hands of the Russians who were racing towards Vienna. Berlin was likely to fall in a matter of days. I could not help feeling sorry for them. For the first time I saw them as a part of the flotsam of war, and I no longer feared them. I could not help wondering how many of them would ever see their families again.

The Italians who had elected or been compelled to fight on the German side behaved without dignity. They swarmed round our convoy clammering for water, vino and cigarettes, none of which they received from our drivers who repelled the advances of their thieving hands with pickaxes and other suitable instruments.

Occasionally we passed a wire cage in which members of the S.S. were confined. These prisoners would later be closely interrogated to discover what crimes could be laid at their door.

About the third day on the road, I was accosted by a dispatch rider coming south. He brought with him a message from Major Thompson instructing me to pull my finger out as the tanks had long since exhausted their ammunition, and might need it when they met our Russian allies coming in the opposite direction. I was to proceed to Klagenfurt in Austria with all haste.

'What's the Major doing?' I asked the D.R.

'Swanning about in his Jeep, requisitioning local wine and spirits for the regiments, and trying to hold on to a luxury hotel in Klagenfurt for the company when it eventually gets there. The Colonel of some other mob is after it for his men and has been trying to pull rank on the Major who has told him to get stuffed, barred all the doors and given instructions to his batman that he's to repel all boarders using force if necessary.'

After consulting the map I saw that Klagenfurt was still over a hundred and fifty miles to the north. Surveying the chaos on the road which could only be compared with the Exeter by-pass in August I instructed my Sergeant to tell the drivers that Klagenfurt was the objective and that they were to proceed there independently with all possible speed. There was to be no dalliance on the way. For once in their lives signorinas, or frauleins as they were now to be called, would take second place. If they got lost on the way, there were plenty of Germans on the road to put them right. Trusting that I would not get into trouble for showing initiative in ordering my convoy to scatter, exhausted by the events of the last few days, I lay down in the back of my truck and left it to Driver Lane and an intelligent Lance Corporal in the front, to get me to Klagenfurt.

Twenty-four hours later I was wakened by the voice of Major Thompson.

'Out of there, you lazy bastard. Come and have a drink and tell me the news. Then I have a most important job for you.'

Tommy took me to the sumptuous hotel which I was glad to see he had held in the face of all opposition. After having a bath and getting Driver Lane to put my uniform into some kind of order, I went down to the bar where Tommy and his officers were drinking schnapps.

They greeted me with congratulations on my success at getting my platoon to Klagenfurt at least two days after the rest of the company had arrived. This was unfair. I had been much further south when the war had ended. I was wounded by their slanders. At least my drivers had not let me down. Each proceeding under his own steam had arrived safely.

Major Tommy drew me to one side. 'How do you feel, Michael?' Not waiting for an answer he continued. 'I want you to take a three tonner immediately and drive tonight to Venice.'

I looked at him incredulously wondering whether the schnapps had gone to his head.

'You will proceed with the truck as far as you can.'

'How do you mean as far as I can?'

'Didn't you know Venice is built on water?'

'I read something about it at school.'

'This is no time for sarcasm,' said Tommy. He handed me a piece of paper on which was written the name of a famous hotel, one at which I had been lucky enough to stay in 1937. 'You will present this official requisition to the Manager or whoever is in charge. It is an order entitling you to remove the entire contents of the wine cellar.'

'This is mad. The Germans will have taken the lot already, or the Eyties will have hidden it, that's for sure.'

'I am not a complete idiot, Michael' said Tommy. 'You are quite right. The entire contents of the cellar have been concealed.'

'That wouldn't have fooled the Germans. Anyway, how did you discover this?'

'Through a certain Lieutenant Mark in Intelligence. He's an American who has been operating behind the lines for some time. He's a first generation American. His parents still live just outside Venice. I swanned into Venice on the way up, and met him at the bar of the Danieli. Under the influence of too much booze he let slip this priceless piece of information. When you reach the hotel, you will find that the cellar beyond the cellar has already been opened up and the contents removed. But what no one has twigged is that there is yet another secret cellar beyond the first secret cellar if you get my meaning. A lot of trouble has gone into its construction and it's protected by a wall at least five feet thick. Don't try to blow it down. The blast might upset the wines.'

'Charming! What about me?'

'You're expendable. This is a highly important mission. It has Brigade's blessing. Speed and security are of the utmost importance. I don't mind telling you, Michael, that Brigade's eyes will be on you. It might even mean a Captaincy. How long have you been a Lieutenant?'

'Tommy,' I said drawing myself to my full height and throwing back another mouthful of schnapps, 'for the first time in my life I have a commanding officer who can see my true abilities beneath my unprepossessing appearance. I shall not fail you',

Tommy wagged his glass at me. 'Speed, Michael, speed. Intelligence at Brigade do not anticipate that Lieutenant Mark will make a move for a few days. There are too many loose bods of all nations swanning around Venice, and he would not dare to expose this Aladdin's Cave to their thieving eyes. He's not in uniform. He looks like an Italian, which of course he is. You, with the full weight of His Majesty's Uniform and this requisition behind you, should have no difficulty.' He held out his hand and we shook hands warmly.

As I made my way back to my platoon it occurred to me that this cache must really be something if my superiors were prepared to send me some one hundred and seventy miles to try to carry it off. I decided that I would take with me Sergeant Jones and a Lance-Corporal fitter by the name of Johnson who was a peace-time prize fighter. I summoned them and let them into the secret, promising them that in the event of a successful outcome to our mission, they should not go unrewarded.

It was now shortly after eleven o'clock in the morning, and I calculated that, allowing for the stream of transport still pouring northward, we could not reach Venice before seven or eight o'clock in the evening. I discarded the idea of trying to make my way down the minor roads, assuming that the bridges would have been blown and not yet repaired.

For once my calculations were not far out. We reached Mestre soon after six and by seven o'clock we were across the causeway and had halted at the station. This was as far as we could go by transport. From now on we would have to be waterborne.

It was a fine May evening. The station was deserted except for a few bands of roving Italian partisans decked out with grenades, bombs, and other pieces of dangerous equipment. They were drunk and like me were looking for some means of transporting themselves into the centre of Venice, no doubt like me too, bent on a few days' looting.

I sent Sergeant Jones and Lance-Corporal Johnson off in search of a boat or gondola, while I kept guard over the lorry. I did not like the way one particularly villainous group of partisans eyed me and it. To show them they would have to pay for it dearly, I took a sub-machine gun out of the cab and ostentatiously clapped on a magazine. This had the desired effect. The partisans sheered off in search of a less redoubtable adversary.

Within ten minutes Sergeant Jones returned.

'There's nothing available. Only a bloody great steamer tied up at the side of the canal. There's an officer in charge of it with a couple of men trying to get up steam. He threatens to blow the head off anybody who tries to come aboard. Apparently the so-called partisans have been giving him trouble.'

Joined by Lance-Corporal Johnson, we made our way through the wrecked station until we came to the canal.

True enough, there was a beautiful vaporetto and by the amount of smoke that was coming out of her funnel, it was clear that she had enough head of steam up to get under way at any moment.

I ran towards her and let out a cry of joy as I saw who was at the helm. It was my old friend Captain John Fish.

Immediately he called out, 'Come aboard. All aboard the *Skylark*.' With which he gave a long blast on the whistle.

I ran to the side, followed by my two men, and we literally jumped aboard as the boat began to pull away from the quay.

I made my way on to the bridge where Driver Jacks, John's batman, immediately put a glass of gin in my hand.

John was having some difficulty in steering a straight course, as he frequently took his eyes off the wheel to ask me about my movements since we had parted company six months earlier.

I decided, in view of the fact that he was in command of a boat that was eminently suitable to my mission, to take him into my confidence, even if it meant promising him a percentage of the booty.

'We attack at dawn' he announced solemnly.

'Why not now?' I asked.

'Are you out of your mind? Thousands and thousands of Italian partisans have been pouring into Venice for the last few days in search of pickings. What with the New Zealanders, Canadians, Americans and South Africans we wouldn't get a single bottle of the stuff out intact. Not a chance. How many men have you?'

'Just these two.'

'With my contingent that makes six.'

'What are you doing here anyway?'

'The company's parked just outside of Mestre. It looks as if we may have to move up to Trieste where Tito and the Jugs are giving trouble. Apart from shooting all the former right wingers, Tito is laying claim to Trieste. Major Hawkins sent me on to Trieste to locate a suitable position of the company and it seemed to me only reasonable to take a look at Venice on the way.'

At this point the sound of the engines turned nasty and, handing me the wheel, John went below to see what the trouble was.

I have never been much good at steering boats. There was a fair wind blowing and it was with the greatest difficulty that I successfully navigated my way through the Ponte Rialto.

We now began to encounter other boats, the odd vaporetto, motor boats filled with drunken soldiers of all nationalities, and gondolas, many of them negotiating as erratic courses as our own craft.

I managed to navigate a sharp left-hand bend contenting myself with removing a few stones from a building I learned many years later to be the Palazzo Giustinian, scraped under the last bridge by the Church of Saint Vitale, and looked like being all set for a safe run to the Square of Saint Mark.

Unfortunately, as I was coming up to the Doge's Palace, the engineers below, no doubt urged on by John, increased the speed of the ship without any request from the bridge.

Desperately I rang the control for them to put the boat into reverse, but either they did not hear me, or the darned thing did not work. I should have kept going. I could have made my way on down to the Lido and out into the safety of the open sea. Instead, I determined to get that wretched boat alongside the Palace if it was the last thing I did.

With a sickening crash, we hit the side of the Grand Canal. There was a splintering of wood and metal. On all sides rose cries of fear. To my horror the vaporetto started to list to the right and began to sink.

'Abandon ship. Abandon ship,' I screamed. There was no nonsense about women and children or other ranks first. I ran forward and with a flying leap put myself on the safety of terra firma.

From behind me I could hear John calling down all the curses he could conjure up.

Luckily no life was lost. A few minutes later we were all safely ashore in front of the Palace.

The vaporetto gave a final lurch, rolled over onto its right side, and half disappeared from view.

John took it all in remarkably good heart. For my part, looking to the future, I could see that it would be something to boast about. Not many people have had the honour of sinking a vaporetto in the Grand Canal.

Many years later, when working for Associated Rediffusion, I had the pleasure of meeting a Lieutenant-Commander who had rivalled my feat. In a thick fog he managed to run his corvette ashore, bringing it to rest on the promenade of a famous south coast resort. As he stepped safely ashore he looked up and saw a notice that read: 'NO PARKING'. It was not so funny for him; their Lordships at the Admiralty had him court-martialled and he was never the same man again.

Our arrival on the shore in front of the Doge's Palace was somewhat marred by the arrival of a posse of Military Police together with the newly appointed Town Major of Venice, who seemed hostile towards both John and myself and was particularly displeased with my poor seamanship.

He became nasty, talked about marching us off to jail, in spite of our protesting that there were a number of Italian partisans roving the canals and up to no good and that he should turn his attention to them. It seemed to me at the time that he was being unnecessarily harsh. But once a copper always a copper.

It was not until I showed him my safe conduct pass signed and stamped several times over that he relented. Warning us not to get into further mischief, he took himself off.

John and I made our way to the Hotel Danieli where we managed to secure accommodation for ourselves and our men. While we were drinking our second bottle of champagne in the bar we were approached by an American in civilian clothing. Addressing himself to me he said: 'Forgive the intrusion, but I saw the flash on your shoulder and was wondering if you knew my friend Major Tommy who was here a couple of days ago.'

'He's my boss,' I said. 'Who are you?'

'Lootenent Mark of American Intelligence.' he announced holding out his hand. 'You see a broken man before you.'

'How is that?'

'We should not be drinking this rubbish' he said pointing towards the bottle of Italian Spumante. 'Ours should be the rightful spoils of the victors. But, alas, I was too late. Those bastard Reds got in before me and cleared the lot.'

'You mean the wine at the . . .?' I said, naming the hotel where Major Thompson had told me the wine had been concealed.

'So you know about it. The whole bloody army knows about it. I should have moved in at once even if it meant fighting my way out with it.'

'Who are these Reds?'

'These ridiculous toy soldiers rushing about with red scarves round their necks, playing at soldiers now that the war is over, calling themselves partisans. Partisans my arse! I've been trying to get the buggers to fight for the last two years and I can tell you that they've shown precious little keenness for it.'

I decided not to tell him that I had come on a similar mission. There seemed no point in upsetting his friendship with Major Thompson by informing him that his friend had taken advantage of his indiscretions and had sent me to filch the prize from under his nose.

'How did they find out about it?' I asked.

'The Communists are everywhere. Could have been a hall porter, a cellarman. No sooner had the Germans pulled out than a contingent of them made straight for the secret cellar, removed its contents and, within a couple of hours, not a trace of a bottle. I must admit that when it comes to thieving, the bastards take some beating. Oh well, there's no point in crying over spilt milk. If you two would care to join me, it would give me great pleasure to show you the sights of Venice.'

'You know it well?' asked John.

'My family still lives here, or just outside. Without any false modesty I am renowned here for my swimming. I used to come here before the war and take part in the swimming championships. In fact I am the swimming champion of Venice. I have many friends here as you will soon discover.'

'Girls?' asked John.

'I am not a homosexual' said Lieutenant Mark coldly.

'Michael is,' said John.

This was one of John's less funny jokes. Because of his technique of always palming me off with the ugly sister, naturally I could not hope to emulate his success. Unfortunately he was able to refer to the open passes that had been made at me by the Regimental Sergeant Major, when we had been wandering around Iraq. John still quotes those memorable words of that wonderful old Regimental Queen who always addressed me as follows: 'Want to be a Captain, Mr Nelson, Sir? If so, my tent at midnight.'

We finished the disgusting Italian champagne and, on being presented with the bill, I signed it, A. Jones, General. This was a common practice in the days following the end of the war.

Our newly acquired American friend certainly knew his way round Venice. We moved from bar to bar. Our conveyance was a fast motor boat, driven and guarded by six tough-looking partisans, decked out with green scarves round their necks. These, Mark informed us, were the right-wing partisans as opposed to the left, who had done most of the fighting behind the enemy lines. I did not fail to notice the scowls that passed between them and the reds. But the latter, although greatly superior in number clearly respected the fighting abilities of our crew and, although they hurled insults at them, made no effort to steal our boat.

39

In Jimmy's Bar Mark was given a warm reception. Bottles of French brandy that had been hoarded through the war years appeared from holes in the ceilings and cracks in the wall. I can recall too a vintage Krug '21, because that year is distinguished for being the year of my birth.

It was at Jimmy's that we started to collect our first bevy of girls. High class girls they were too. Not the scrubbers that usually fell to my lot.

Mark gave me a magnificent build-up. 'This young Tenente,' he told the throng that gathered around us stroking our hair when they were not planting impassioned kisses on our lips, 'this young Tenente is the most formidable lion in the whole of the British Army. Together with the brave Capitano he was dropped behind the German lines. I have seen him strangle twenty *tedeschi* with his own hands.' At which point the girls vied with one another to seize my nicotine-stained hands and raise them tenderly to their lips. 'Believe, me, the Capitano is a brave man, but the young Tenente is a lion.'

At this point I thought I was going to be lucky enough to be raped simultaneously by ten Venetian girls. Naturally by now all thought of duty had evaporated. I no longer cared about the failure of my mission, and how I should explain everything to Major Thompson and the big wigs at Brigade. The fact that I had failed through no fault of my own did not affect the issue. An order had been given and in military circles there can be no extenuating circumstances. Many were the high-ranking officers demoted, or on occasions promoted sideways into some boring job, because they had lost a battle which the Almighty could not have won. Subsequently, along would come some flashy general fresh from the United Kingdom, and because everything was in his favour both tactically and logistically, win the next battle, be promoted Field-Marshal and showered with letters after his name. It was a lesson the military had learnt from the execution of Admiral Byng. Only success will be regarded. Failure will be punished. The system did away with the waste of time caused by long inquests, and on the whole worked very well.

I think that night in Venice is the most memorable of all my 52 years, I was completely happy. Who could fail to be, surrounded by girls of all shades, each one competing with the next for the honour of bestowing her favours upon me. Titians, blondes, brunettes, they were all there. Looking back on that night I can recall too with particular pleasure the look of amazement not untinged with envy in John Fish's eyes. Ever since that night Venice has been my favourite city, and I still cannot cross its causeway without a stirring in the pit of my stomach. Most people go to Venice for culture, to get aching feet walking round its art galleries, palaces and churches. I go there in the faint hope that the events of that most glorious night may be repeated. They never can be.

It would be unseemly to go into the intimate details of what occurred on my return to the Hotel Danieli. It could decently be described as the most hilarious and sexy kaleidoscope, a grand mêlée of flesh, hair and champagne, the last name being a crate of the real French stuff which Mark procured and insisted on bringing to my room declaring that only with its aid would I be able to uphold the honour of the British Army.

It was many years later that I first heard the expression, 'Three in a bed leads to bickering'. While this may be true I can honestly say that from the experience of that one night, ten in a bed can lead to nothing but joy and harmony. With no wish to boast of sexual prowess, indeed my memoirs have on the whole rather regrettably recalled only too often my failure to put up any kind of show, I can honestly say that Tenente Nelson exceeded even his own wildest dreams on that splendid night.

The next thing I remember was being shaken on the shoulder, opening my eyes, and looking up into the startled face of Sergeant Jones. On all sides of me, on top of me, beneath me, alongside me were acres of smooth skinned female flesh.

'Stone the bloody crows,' was all that Sergeant Jones could say. 'Now I know it's true.'

'What's true?'

'About you having it away with all those whores in the knocking shop in Alex at the same time.'

I felt a thousand feet high as I dragged my feet from the bed to the floor. No man minds his virility being praised and I knew that Sergeant Jones would not be slow to pass on the information to the men of my platoon, who would be impressed and happy to obey my orders without question or dalliance.

'I think we ought to be on the road, or rather the water, Sir,' continued Sergeant Jones. 'I don't like the smell of it here one little bit. Those bloody partisans are getting out of hand loosing off in all directions.'

To confirm his words there came a burst of Bren fire much too close to the Danieli for my liking. It occurred to me how ridiculous it would be to be killed by a partisan's stray bullet after having so successfully engineered a safe path through five years of warfare.

'How do we get out of here?' I asked.

One of the girls put her arms round my neck and pulled me down on top of her, whispering what I assumed to be sweet Italian nothings into my ear. At the same time two others began to caress my back and thighs.

'Stone the bloody crows,' repeated Sergeant Jones.

'What am I to do, Sergeant?' I asked managing to turn towards him.

'Tell you what, Sir. Give you another half-hour. Lieutenant Mark has placed his motor boat at our disposal. Which reminds me, Sir, both he and Captain Fish wish to be remembered to you, and asked me to say good-bye to you on their behalf, as they're both otherwise engaged, like you, Sir, if you get my meaning. Captain Fish in particular said I'm to tell you that he hoped you'd remembered to write your name on the soles of your boots.'

I returned to my luscious girls, and within the next half an hour did my best to give each of the darlings something to remember their lion of a Tenente by in the years to come.

Three-quarters of an hour later, flanked by Sergeant Jones and Lance-Corporal Johnson, both of whom gave me valiant support, I staggered towards our waiting craft. As we approached it, its green-scarfed crew raised a cheer.

'What's this in aid of?'

'News of your prowess has gone ahead, Sir. There's a movement afoot to make you an honorary citizen of the city of Venice.'

I boarded the craft to shouts of '*Viva Casanova*', but failed to distinguish myself by collapsing to the bottom of the boat as Sergeant Jones and Lance-Corporal Johnson let go of my arms.

As we drew away from the side of the Grand Canal, two officers of the British Army in full uniform, walked slowly to its edge. Without a pause, without a word, they dived fully clothed into the water and started to strike out for the opposite bank.

I still love Venice. I love its canals, its backwaters, its churches, its paintings. But it is not for these that it is forever engraved on my heart, but for mountains of lovely flesh, and two officers diving into the Grand Canal. You could say that I nearly died a most beautiful death in Venice.

It must have been towards three o'clock on the same afternoon when I was sleeping in the back of the three-tonner as we were making our way northwards towards Klagenfurt that I was woken by Sergeant Jones.

'Mr Harrison wants to speak to you, Sir'.

Lieutenant Harrison was my opposite number who commanded the second platoon of the Transport Company.

'Harry? What the devil is he doing?' I said trying to recall where I was.

I clambered out of the back of the lorry, and was greeted by Harry exclaiming: 'Christ Almighty, what have you been up to?'

I decided that the more alluring details could await a larger audience in the Officer's Mess. I noticed that trucks of his platoon were going past at high speed in a southerly direction.

'There's a flap on' said Harry.

'What do you mean a flap, Harry? The war's over, isn't it?'

'That silly bugger Tito. He's trying to grab Trieste. Brigade's been ordered to a place just outside called Udine to stand by in case of trouble.'

'Where are we?'

'You *are* in a state,' said Harry. 'Your're just on the Italian side of the border.'

'With Yugoslavia?'

'No, you nit, with Austria. Don't you remember you were in Klagenfurt the day before yesterday? By the way Tommy's mad keen to hear how you got on with the wine.'

'He'll be madder still when I tell him what happened,' I said. 'What about my platoon?'

'They left soon after you did. They should be somewhere round Udine by now.'

'Give me the war any day,' I said. Turning to Sergeant Jones I repeated the magical formula which must be learned early on by all young Lieutenants. 'Carry on, Sergeant. Wake me when we get to Udine.'

It was about midnight when Sergeant Jones, having faithfully carried out my orders, roused me from a deep sleep into which I had fallen in the back of the truck lying upon a bale of camouflage nets.

'All's well, Sir.'

I clambered out of the truck having regathered much of my strength, and feeling much better than when we had left Venice that morning.

My platoon was parked-up in a vineyard, and from the noise coming from the back of the trucks it was clear to me that some of my drivers were making the most of the previous year's harvest.

Sergeant Jones conducted me to the villa: 'The men are sleeping in their trucks,' he explained. 'There are a lot of light fingered so-called partisans in the area, and the one thing they want to do is knock off some form of transport to carry the loot off in. But I thought it would be more comfortable to establish Platoon Headquarters in the villa. It belongs to a Count and a Contessa, and from all reports she's just your cup of tea, Sir. Really smart bit of goods so the lads tell me.'

'She will have to wait till the morning,' I replied loftily.

43

'Another thing, Sir. Major Thompson says you're to report to him as soon as you arrive. Driver Lane is standing by with a fifteen-hundred-weight to take you right away.'

I had not taken Driver Lane with me on my expedition to Venice because, much as I admired him as a batman and general scrounger, I rated his fighting capacities on a level with my own.

I found him waiting outside and, although it was dark, I was amazed to notice that he threw me up a salute, something that he had omitted to do for the last two years.

'Are you feeling all right?' I enquired.

'Are *you* all right, Sir?' he asked. He could not conceal his curiosity. 'Is it true what Sergeant Jones and Corporal Johnson have been saying, Sir?'

'What have they been saying?' I said, trying to throw the line away.

'Come off it, Sir. About you and those twenty bints all in a bed at the same time. They say you serviced . . .'

'That's enough,' I said. 'You should not listen to idle gossip.' By saying this, by adopting a pose of false modesty, I was certain that my reputation, together with my popularity, would be assured.

'I'm so glad, Sir. That'll put Mr Harrison's batman in his place. He's always boasting what a superman Mr Harrison is and saying that everyone except me knows you're a pansy.'

'Drive on, Driver,' I said stepping into the front of the fifteen-hundred-weight.

Major Thompson had established Company Headquarters in Udine together with the rest of the Brigade. I noticed that quite a number of its tanks were parked round the centre of the town. There was clearly a real flap on as they must have been brought back south from Klagenfurt on tank transporters.

'Where are the rest of the officers?' I asked the sentry on the door.

'All kipped down, Sir. Had a hell of a time getting down here, and everybody's just about had it. It was a darned sight better when we were chasing Jerry.'

A few minutes later I went into Major Thompson's room.

'Sit down, Michael.' he said. 'Sorry to ask you to report to me as soon as you got in. The situation's serious.'

'About the wine, Sir . . .'

'Have you got it with you?'

'No, Sir. I'm sorry, Sir, but someone got there before me.'

'Too bad,' said Tommy.

Because he did not give me hell, I knew the situation was bad.

44

'Forget about the wine for now. You can tell me about it later.' He walked to a map hanging on the wall. 'We're here . . . Trieste's some fifty-five miles to the south-west. As you know Tito's giving trouble and trying to take over the place, which neither we nor the Americans want. He's our ally as you know, so we want to avoid a confrontation if possible. The trouble is that we're very thin on the ground. Half the Brigade is pressing on from Klagenfurt towards Vienna, but it looks as if we're too late already and the Ruskis are already there and in full control. The whole situation has now become political, and it looks as if we're going to lose out on every side because the Americans refused to listen to Churchill and are stupid enough to believe that the Russians have no territorial claims to make in Western Europe. No one here at Brigade seems to know what's going to happen, but it may be necessary for us to move with the New Zealand Brigade into Trieste. I've just come back from Brigade, and you'll be pleased to hear that there's no ammo for the tanks if we do have to move. But I gather there is a fair supply at a dump in Ferrara.'

'I know it well. I was loading there the day the war finished, whenever that was. It seems a year away to me.'

'I've given your platoon a few hours' rest. Harry's off with his to scrounge some petrol. I know they've had a hell of a few days, but I want you to go back and get your drivers on the road to Ferrara right away. Oh, that's another thing. You'll have to go in convoy. Those bloody Eytie partisans are hi-jacking single vehicles. If you have any trouble with them don't hesitate to shoot. There won't be any questions asked. Your men will take their rifles with them and see they load them, but for God's sake make sure they put the safety catches on. Hold a rifle inspection before you leave in case some silly sod has put one up the spout. Harry nearly got killed this morning by one of the cooks. Not that it was the cook's fault. He told me he'd never handled a gun—yes, he called it a gun—since he was in the training battalion five years ago. Well, that's that. I expect before you go you'd like a quick drink. You may be interested in this brandy. Austrian, but quite drinkable.'

While we were drinking the brandy I told Tommy of my adventures in Venice, not of course mentioning what had occurred at the Hotel Danieli. I reckoned that the news would soon come to him via the Lance-Corporal in charge of the Officer's Mess, and I felt that to recount the full story myself would lay me open to a charge of boasting.

Tommy was very good about my failure to bring back the wine, although in accordance with normal procedure, he pointed out that it was entirely my fault; that I should have proceeded with greater haste and not dallied on the road. I took this reprimand in the spirit in which it was administered, and once again said good-bye to my Captaincy.

Shortly after two o'clock in the morning, two hours before daylight, my thirty lorries were on the road rumbling southwards over the ground we had covered only a few days before in pursuit of the retreating Germans.

There was a fair amount of grumbling, and a certain amount of rejigging of drivers had to be accomplished by the platoon N.C.O.'s so that those who were drunk should not be allowed at the wheel until they had sobered up.

I never did succeed in teaching my drivers not to treat the local wines in the same way as they would beer. They insisted in drinking it by the pint, always with disastrous results. They even managed to down sweet Marsala by the pint without being sick on the spot.

One of the most tragic sights I ever saw in the course of the Italian campaign was one of my Lance-Corporals 'playing' Cardinal Puff under Captain John Fish's tuition.

This is an awful game. The Master of Ceremonies is called Cardinal Puff, and he goes through a series of deliberate movements as he drinks, maybe raising his glass twice, knocking it on the table twice, raising it to his lips and taking it away before drinking. Quite a complicated sequence. The wretched novitiate has to copy each of these movements accurately. The slightest deviation and his glass is immediately filled to the brim and he has to start again from the beginning. This ritual was carried out with great beakers of wine, and naturally the aspirant was soon hopelessly drunk. It was quite an honour to succeed, when one became a Cardinal Puff oneself and was entitled to inflict this horrible punishment on other people.

This particular Lance-Corporal's greatest ambition in life was to be elected to the Brotherhood of Cardinal Puff. Unfortunately he just could not drink. He was one of those drivers who got drunk at the whiff of the barmaid's apron. As for doing it in wine, he didn't stand a chance. On this occasion, after he had failed yet again, it was my misfortune to see him rolling about on the ground, vomiting copiously, with the tears pouring down his cheeks as he sobbed: 'But I want to be Cardinal Puff. I want to be Cardinal Puff.'

It was very strange driving southwards on that early May morning, passing all the debris and aftermath of war. It has always amazed me the way a country which has been ravaged by war can rise again and conceal what would seem at the time to be unhealable scars. On all sides were the charred remains of the machines of war, tanks, trucks, motor-cycles,

46

guns. Everywhere were scattered thousands and thousands of pieces of equipment, helmets, knapsacks, ammunition pouches. Now and again beside the road was a recently erected cross or rows of crosses stuck into newly turned mounds of earth. They made me feel very sad.

All the villages through which we passed were in a state of devastation and again I found it incredible, when I went back to Italy some years after the war, to see them completely rebuilt.

We drove into Padua at about seven in the morning, and pulled up in the main square to brew up and have breakfast.

We had just started to eat our food, when a band of partisans appeared in the square escorting some pitiful specimens of both sexes. The men had clearly been very badly beaten up. Now and again one of the guards would crash his rifle butt down on their heads, or thrash them across the backs with heavy rods. The women's heads had been shaved, and now and again one of the partisans would prance up to them screaming abuse and proceed to eject a mouthful of spittle over them.

This disgusted my drivers and they were all for interfering. I did not know what to do, as I had no idea how many other partisans might be lurking in the vicinity and would come to the assistance of their brave comrades if we attacked.

However, the decision was taken out of my hands. With one accord my drivers pulled back the bolts of their rifles and bunged one up the spout. Without a word from me they advanced upon the disgusting circus, and quietly confronted it. It was quite clear to these heroic Italians what they had in mind. They immediately let their prisoners go and slunk away from the square swearing revenge upon my intrepid drivers. I was very proud of them and wish this incident to be inscribed on the battle honours of the Royal Army Service Corps.

There was little we could do to help the prisoners, who begged us to take them along as well. This we did, and at their request dropped them in the hilly country outside the city. I learned later that they were rounded up again and shot.

The rest of the journey to Ferrara was accomplished without further incident. We loaded up the ammunition and by midnight were back in Udine, where we delivered it to the tanks. I believe they rumbled off in the direction of Trieste to support the New Zealand Brigade who had already moved there to confront our erstwhile allies. We remained in Udine, ready if necessary to follow them should our supply services be required.

Chapter Four

Life in the Villa Foreste soon assumed a happy rhythm, smoothly regulated by my platoon sergeants whom I left well alone. I saw no point in throwing everything out of gear by interfering.

I rose at eight, by which time most of the trucks had departed from the vineyards to service the various units of the Brigade which were still in the area and had not moved up to Trieste. Driver Lane would then serve me breakfast on the verandah of the villa, and I made an effort to catch up on my correspondence. This consisted of writing to my family.

Although I had been a young literary lion before joining the army, I now found myself completely out of touch with my former friends and acquaintances who had been lucky enough either to avoid the services, or had managed to obtain permanent home postings. I don't want to drag up old scores, and I know it is unfashionable to question people's motives in a war that finished years and years ago, but I would like to place it on record that the Ministry of Information was an absolute godsend for middle and upper class intellectuals who preferred to contribute to the war effort there rather than in the forces.

Sometimes, with Driver Lane at the wheel of my fifteen-hundred-weight I would drive round the countryside, stopping now and again to see how my drivers fared, and to warn them if there were Military Police in the area, if they were not bent on lawful duty, which was very often indeed.

Lunch I usually ate at Headquarters with Major Thompson and the other officers of the company. Provided that the pre-lunch session of gin and water had not been too overpowering, after a short siesta the late afternoon would be devoted to poker, which would continue until about eight in the evening when there would be a break for further refreshment.

About a fortnight after my return from Venice, my interest in the opposite sex began to reawaken. Who shall blame it? It was a glorious spring and the weather was warm. The only thing to mar it was that I had noticed a stirring of bull. Peace had broken out and unless I was mistaken the regulars were already determined to get the army back onto peace-time lines, and eliminate all the slackness and bad habits that had been brought in by the civilian element. I don't suppose that they considered for one moment that without the civilians they would never have won the war, and that most of them owed their elevation to the highest ranks to the vast number of these temporary soldiers drafted in for the duration.

It started in small ways. I have just mentioned the harrassment of my drivers by posses of Military Police speeding around the country in Jeeps, putting their noses into the backs of lorries to see if anything unauthorized was being carried. Unauthorized goods included the local signorinas, whom my drivers rightly considered to be the fair spoils of the victors. Up to now they had carried them openly in the cabs. Now that they were not even permitted to carry them in the rear, they were rightly indignant.

One morning as I was wandering through the main street of Udine with my mind veering towards the opposite sex, wondering where the best pick-up was likely to be made, I was stopped by a Captain in the Military Police, who remarked on the absence of a hat and demanded to what regiment I owed the honour of wearing a yellow and blue scarf round my neck. I was so dumbfounded that I informed him that I was a member of Groppis Light, seconded to the Shepheard's Horse, information which he took in poor part. The fellow clearly had no sense of humour. Finally I imparted to him my true identity, which he jotted down in a note book, telling me that I should hear further.

I knew that matters were serious when Tommy summoned us to his presence one morning, and with a look of anguish on his face informed us that a new Brigade Major had arrived and had already expressed his horror at the absence of fire buckets throughout the Brigade lines, and in particular in the lines of my platoon. I could not argue, for I had an inbuilt antipathy to fire buckets. The few times I had been compelled to display them back in the Old Country my drivers had insisted on using them either as ash trays or as public conveniences. The idea of setting up rows of red painted buckets between the vines seemed to me to be ludicrous and I said as much to Tommy.

'I'm sorry, Michael,' he said 'that's the way it's going to be. As you know I've decided to stay on in the army instead of going back to the Bank. I'm a Major now, and I want to stay that way. So I'll arse-lick anyone to whom I have to perform that unsavoury service.'

I reminded Tommy of the conundrum: 'Why is the British Army like a pomegranate?' The answer is: 'Because you get more pips by sucking.'

It was with forebodings that I left that conference. I knew I could not expect to be released from the army for at least a year, possibly more, on account of my tender age. The army would hang on to me till the last moment. Whereas in the piping days of war I had been able to get away with murder, it would be very different now. Ahead of me I could see nothing but trouble, Summaries of Evidence, Courts Martial. About the latter I was not worried provided that they ended with my dishonourable discharge. But there was always the danger of being reduced to the ranks and sent to the glasshouse, and that scared me a great deal. So I decided to mend my ways, give a great deal of thought to the dangers ahead, and lay my plans accordingly.

As I approached my platoon lines mulling over these problems, I noticed groups of roving partisans, all heavily armed, lurking around the perimeter. As I drove up to the villa I noticed that the guards had been doubled.

Sergeant Jones was waiting for me: 'These silly buggers with red scarves want to search the villa. I've told 'em to piss off. I've put any extra bods I could find on duty. I've got out the Boys Anti-Tank. As we've lugged the sods all round the Middle East and all the way up Italy, nothing would give me more pleasure than to loose it off at these silly sods.'

'What's the trouble?'

'I gather they're after the Count. They say he was a Fascist big wig. The Contessa's in a hell of a state and wants you to go upstairs and see her right away.'

I ran up to the first floor which we had left in the occupation of the Contessa and her household, my platoon headquarters having taken over the ground floor.

Up to this point I had had few dealings with the lady. All I knew was that she spoke perfect English, was very beautiful and clearly wanted to keep herself to herself.

I found her sitting by the window in the drawing room. She was holding a handkerchief to her face, and although I could not see any tears, she looked even more beautiful in this state of distress.

'Contessa, what's the trouble?' I asked sitting down as close as possible to her without wishing to cause her any offence.

'It is my husband. He is a good man, Tenente. Now these wicked Reds come and seek him to take him away to kill him. But he never did anyone any harm.'

'Where is your husband?'

'I do not know,' she said. 'When the war comes he goes away. Maybe the Germans take him with them. Maybe the Fascists take him.' Her voice broke. 'Maybe he is dead.'

This was too much for me. I have never been able to stand the sight of a lady in tears.

With true British improvisation I said: 'What about a cup of tea?' 'How rude of me, Tenente. You work so hard all the time, and now I ask you to share my troubles.' She put her white hand on my nicotine-stained fingers. I reminded myself to tell Driver Lane to search the town for a piece of pumice stone.

'Perhaps you would ring the bell?' she said.

I did as she commanded and almost immediately her Major Domo was inside the door, bowing.

'Some tea please, Antonio,' she said. Turning to me she added: 'I fear it will only be Indian.'

'There isn't an Army issue of China,' I replied before I could check myself.

She smiled. 'Ah, yes, your Corporal Cook has been most gracious to us. Without him we would have starved.'

Knowing my Corporal Cook's liking for beautiful women I must confess that a nasty suspicion crossed my mind, and I wondered if I was the cuckold of the century and last in the queue for the Contessa's favours.

When Antonio had retired to bring up the tea she continued: 'And your Sergeant Jones. He is a hero. He would not allow these dreadful Reds into the house.' Once again she touched me gently on the hand, opened her dark eyes wide and I felt a shiver pass through my body. 'You would not allow those dreadful Reds into my villa, would you, my dear Tenente?'

'Never! They shall not pass,' I replied resolutely, curling my fingers round her hand and appreciating its softness. She let it rest there and made no effort to take it away.

'How stupid all this war has been,' she continued. 'Why should people like you and me, cultured people like ourselves, ever dream of fighting one another?'

I had heard this line often before during my slog up Italy and it was not one that greatly pleased me. I found the attempts of the Italian upper classes to dissociate themselves from the war irritating, as in nearly every case they were the people who had benefited most from Mussolini's régime.

However, on this particular occasion I was not willing to spoil my chances with the Contessa, and with all the gallantry at my command I replied: 'I have no quarrel with you, Contessa.' Then giving her hand a gentle squeeze I continued: 'I am sure you and I can become very good friends.'

I spoiled the effect by adding 'With your husband away, I don't think a woman like you should be on her own.'

Anyway, she took it the wrong way and I found myself looking down at an empty hand. A further exchange of intimacies was interrupted by the arrival of Antonio bearing the tea and some thinly cut bully beef sandwiches.

We spent a happy hour together discussing the English season in peace time, about which I knew absolutely nothing. However, I was quite an expert on horses, as our family house had been at Ascot opposite the race course, and I threw in the names of the odd Baron and Viscount, and hinted that I was not unrelated to the great Lord Nelson of Trafalgar fame. This, I could see, impressed her greatly, and when the time came for me to withdraw, I felt pretty certain that I had considerably forwarded my suit and it was merely a matter of waiting for the ripe fruit to drop from the bough.

During the following days I kept a heavy guard on the platoon lines and, although the Reds still skulked ceaselessly round the camp, they made no effort to attack it. At the same time I continued to lay siege to the Contessa's affections, and did not let a morning, afternoon or evening pass without in some way trying to show her the nature of my affection for her. One morning I would bring her highly prized tins of Spam exchanged with some wondering Americans for half a bottle of Scotch. In fact it was only a quarter bottle, because half of it was distilled water obtained from our Workshops Section. It is very important to use distilled water, because ordinary water gives the fluid a greasy consistency and the game away into the bargain.

On other occasions I would present her with a posy of spring flowers, which Driver Lane picked between the rows of vines. On other occasions I would see that she was supplied with a cut off the joint, now that we were receiving an issue of fresh meat, the first for many months. Each time I brought her my offerings I made enquiries about the Count.

'I fear the worst,' she would reply.

'Never mind, I will look after you,' I said, as I sank in the chair by her side and gently took her hand in mine.

Looking back at those spring days of 1945 it is easy to laugh. Indeed there were not a few men in my platoon who found the sight of Captain Blossom in love ludicrous. Even today I sometimes believe that I really did fall in love with the Contessa. She had an ethereal quality about her which appealed to the poet in me. She reawakened some memories of tenderness and delicacy that had been effaced by over four years of military life. Above all she really was beautiful, the most beautiful woman I have ever met in my life.

On all sides there were bets and counter-bets as to when I should make base. One faction of drivers reckoned I was too soft on the Contessa, that the full frontal approach which had distinguished me in Venice, was the answer. Others reckoned that I was playing it the right way, that the Contessa was a lady of breeding and refinement, and that my starry-eyed technique would bring me my due reward in the end.

One evening after my siesta I was strolling down the main street of Udine peering into the windows of the ill-stocked shops, searching for some acceptable gift for the apple of my eye, when I was hailed by someone shouting:

'Hi there! If it isn't Casanova himself.'

The next moment Lieutenant Mark of American Intelligence was pumping my hand up and down. 'Well, isn't this just great? Whoever thought I'd run into you son-of-a-bitch in this one-horse town.'

'What are you doing here?'

'Highly secret work, Mike. Highly secret.'

He then proceeded to tell me that he had been sent to Udine for two purposes—to winkle out the big time fascists who had gone to ground, and to set about disarming the roving bands of partisans who were terrorizing the countryside and behaving like bandits.

Soon we were going over the remarkable events of our night out in Venice, and he told me that my reputation was still high in that city.

'What do you do about dames here?' he asked.

'Nothing.'

He looked at me incredulously.

I did not feel like telling Mark that I was in love. Instead I said: 'Nothing much here that I fancy.'

'Is that so? Just you come with me, Mike, and we'll soon put that right.'

Before I could protest he took me by the arm and more or less frog-marched me down the street talking all the time.

Finally we came to a small hotel off the main street. At the door stood a group of partisans, all heavily armed.

'Welcome to American Intelligence Headquarters,' said Mark as he propelled me past the guards into the hotel.

The foyer of the hotel was packed with civilians, mostly women, women of all ages, shapes and sizes.

Giving me a wink, and roughly pushing his way through them, Mark crossed the foyer and went into the room which originally must have been the lounge and which was now being used as an office.

Mark slouched down behind a desk and indicated that I was to take one of the armchairs.

'God, what a life,' he exclaimed. 'Can't see how I'll ever sort this lot out. What a shower! What a bloody shower!' He motioned towards the door. 'See that crowd out there. Not one of them was fascist. Not one of them.' He started to mimic. 'Oh no, Tenente, my husband always an anti-fascist. He always against Mussolini.'

'Were they?' I asked.

'How the hell should I know? The partisans have clapped hundreds of them in the gaol and it's my job to sort them out, decide who should be tried and who should go free. What an impossible task! One bloody little Lieutenant in American Intelligence has to hand down the judgement of twenty Solomons.'

Mark ran his hand through his thick hair, grinned and said: 'Anyway, take your pick. Fifteen, twenty, thirty-year-olds. They're all out there ready for plucking provided you promise to get their fathers, husbands, what have you, out of gaol. They're scared stiff the partisans may run wild and knock them off out of hand. In fact I've reason to believe they have already shot quite a number.'

It seems strange to have to report that I was shocked. Strange because in the course of the war I had had my fair share of whores. I had known Mary's House well, and the brothels of Naples, Rome and the larger cities had all received my custom. Somehow the prospect of taking one of those miserable girls waiting outside in the hall in exchange for promising to release some member of their family, seemed to be obscene in the extreme.

'Listen, Mike, I guess I'll get myself a bath before I get down to work. What you want to do? Say what, let's pick ourselves a couple and get them to scrub us down and anything else you fancy. What about the little blonde bit? She can't be more than seventeen'.

It wasn't a new-found sense of morality that made me hold back. I was thinking of my adorable Contessa and how much I loved her. So I said, 'I'd love a bit right now, but I must report to my Headquarters ten minutes ago.'

'Please yourself, Mike,' he said opening the door. The crowd of women swept towards him, holding out their hands and pleading with him.

'Get back, you fucking bastards,' he roared. Looking round he saw the little blonde girl. He grabbed her roughly round the waist. 'Come on, my bella,' he shouted at her. 'Show me how you can work and we'll then decide if your daddy's a fascist or not.'

Pushing his way through the beseeching crowd he ran up the stairs dragging her with him. When he reached the top of the stairs he turned and shouted down to me: 'Say Mike, why not come back later this

54

evening and we'll get outselves a ball. What do you fancy—blonde, brunette, or both at the same time?'

When I reached my platoon lines I put all ideas of an orgy out of my mind and made my way to the Contessa's apartment to speak with her of true love. On the landing I was met by Antonio who told me that the Contessa was not well, had a headache, and did not wish to be disturbed. I don't know what it was, but there was something shifty in the way he spoke to me, and against all inclinations I had a feeling that the Contessa was trying to avoid me. Up to this point she had never refused to see me, if only because she was anxious to see what gifts I might be bringing her, whether Spam, bully beef or cigarettes.

Somewhat put out I returned downstairs and ordered Driver Lane to find Sergeant Jones and a bottle of some strong poison.

A few minutes later Sergeant Jones appeared with a bottle of Scotch. He saluted, sat down, and placed the bottle on the table.

'I think that would be better for us than Eytie gut rot, Sir,' he said.

'Where did you get it from?' I asked.

Supplies of the real stuff had been remarkably short recently, even to units of the R.A.S.C.

'Have a sister working in the NAAFI, Sir,' he said winking at me.

He leant forward and poured out two glasses. Raising his he said: 'Cheers. Anything the matter, Sir? I trust nothing serious, as everything seems to be jogging along nicely except for bastard M.P.'s sticking their bloody noses in everywhere.'

'I'm not at all happy, Sergeant.'

'You don't have to tell me or anybody else round here for that matter, Sir. If you don't mind me saying so the worst thing His Majesty ever did was to make you an officer.'

'So you don't think I'm officer material, Sergeant?'

'Officer material! You're not bloody driver material, Sir.'

'Thank you very much, Sergeant,' I said. 'For your information I was not referring to the failure of my military career, which I have made no effort to conceal.'

'You couldn't if you tried, if I may say so, Sir.'

Ignoring Sergeant Jones' comment I continued: 'I am deeply concerned about my relationship with the Contessa . . .'

'What a bint!'

'What a bint as you so delicately express it, Sergeant. The fact of the matter is I have a feeling that she's trying to avoid me. After all the rich gifts I've brought her I find this disturbing. When I think of the favours

55

that many members of this platoon have procured for half a tin of bully beef and a couple of cigarette ends, I am even more upset.'

Sergeant Jones looked me squarely in the eyes. 'Do you want it straight from me, Sir?'

'Straight.'

'You're making a right soft prick of yourself.'

Whereas I appreciated the turn of phrase I was not altogether delighted with its implications.

'Proceed further, Sergeant.'

'She doesn't fancy you, Sir.'

'How do you know?'

'Look, Sir, you've been giving her the royal treatment. You don't have to cover up, I know just how many rations you have been sending into her daily, apart from the other odds and ends. Bully, jam, odd bottle of Scotch, not to mention half the bloody company's tea ration. Well, it stands to reason if she were going to give in she would have given in by now. You're meant to be an educated man, Sir. Frankly I reckon the dumbest driver in the platoon would have done better than you.'

'How do you mean?'

'You've got to change your tactics, Sir. Have you considered a frontal assault?'

'Never did approve of those First War tactics. Too many casualties.'

'Which reminds me, Sir. Corporal Johnson's got a dose of the clap.'

'Bloody careless of him.'

'I've had the offending signorina posted out of bounds, Sir.'

'For goodness sake lets talk about Corporal Johnson some other time,' I said, annoyed with Sergeant Jones for so much as associating the woman I loved with the disease which the unfortunate Corporal had caught. 'So you think I should be more direct?'

'That's my opinion, Sir, and I think the majority of the platoon would support it.'

'I'm glad to hear the men have my welfare at heart, Sergeant.'

'You would be surprised how many lire have been wagered on it,' said Sergeant Jones.

'As a matter of academic interest, Sergeant, what do you think?'

'You'll never bloody make it, Sir. Not a bloody chance. These high class Eyties are all the same. Promise you the earth and what do you get? Not so much as a sniff. If they were really hungry like the rest of the Wops you might be in with a chance. But they're too well-heeled. No, Sir, you don't stand a chance with the classy crumpet round here.'

I had great respect for Sergeant Jones and his appreciation of any given situation. So it was in a very depressed mood that I went into the mess in Udine that evening.

Not even Tommy, who was in sparkling form having just heard that he had been awarded the O.B.E., could cheer me up. Not even the constant references to Other Buggers' Efforts, each one followed with a deep libation of gin, could lift me from my introspective state of mind. Sergeant Jones had said I did not stand a chance, and I was a great believer in Sergeant Jones. For the first time I was in love, as opposed to in lust.

'What the devil's the matter with you tonight?' asked Major Thompson as we finally left the ante-room and made our way into the mess for dinner.

'Haven't you heard, Tommy? Michael's in love. He's fallen for the beautiful Contessa Foreste,' said Harry, not realizing the depth of my ill humour.

'Listen Harry, if you want to make something of it, you can come outside right now and I'll do my best to sort you out, you gin-sodden crutch,' I said angrily.

Major Thompson stepped between us, pushing Harry away from me. He put his arm round me and said: 'Quieten down, lads. You can tell uncle Tommy all about it at dinner.' Taking me by the arm he led me round the table and sat me down next to him.

'Thanks, Tommy,' I said. 'Don't worry, I won't bore you. I'll get well and truly sloshed instead.'

'Do that thing, Mike,' he said.

'You're a great guy, Tommy,' I said, 'If only every officer of Field Rank was like you it would have been a pleasure to have served in this stinking Corps in this bloody war. God how I hate it all.'

'For Christ's sake don't get maudlin,' he said.

Harry, who had seated himself next to me, touched me on the arm. 'Sorry, old man, didn't mean to offend you. Accept my apologies and all that crap.'

'Accepted, old man,' I said. 'After all, the two oldest and most useless subalterns in the British Army should never fall out.'

'I drink to that,' said Harry.

During the rest of the meal I cheered up as Harry and I recounted stories of how subalterns much junior to ourselves had climbed their way upwards, many of them reaching Field Rank.

'The trouble with us, Mike,' said Harry, 'is that we're too independent. We're non-conformists. In fact, if we had been given independent commands we would have turned out brilliant soldiers and now be covered with real gongs not like that piece of shit Tommy's been awarded.'

I think Tommy was somewhat annoyed by this reference to his O.B.E. because he turned to us and said, 'The trouble with both of you is that you're the worst officers it has ever been my misfortune to command. Besides you drink too much.'

Harry let out a roar of laughter. 'Listen who's calling the kettle black. Did you hear that, Mike?'

'Tommy's a lovely man, Harry,' I said. 'Leave him alone.'

'If I didn't know you better, Mike, I'd say you were nothing but a ruddy queer,' said Harry.

'So I am, dear' I said.

'Who's for poker after dinner?' said Tommy.

During the game of poker that seemed to go on for hours and hours, my ill humour returned. I could only focus my mind on the Contessa and not on the cards, with the result that I lost heavily and consistently.

After playing for only an hour Tommy turned to me and said, 'Listen, Mike, you're not up to it tonight. You're spoiling the game for the rest of us. Why don't you call it a day and turn in early tonight for a change?'

I was very grateful to Tommy. I stood back from the table, bade good night, and made my way out to the street where Driver Lane was already waiting for me.

'Made a right bloody fool of yourself tonight didn't you, losing all that money?' he said. 'Don't worry, I've left enough with the Mess Corporal to square your debts.'

'Where do you get it all from?'

'It grows on bloody trees, doesn't it?' he said.

He helped me into the truck, and I sat back in the seat while he drove out of Udine back to my platoon lines.

I don't think I had ever seen Sergeant Jones ruffled before, but he certainly was that night. He was waiting for me in the platoon Headquarters room as I staggered in.

'Just about bloody time too,' he said. 'Didn't the D.R. reach you at Company Headquarters?'

'What D.R.?'

'Don't say the bloody fool didn't get there.'

'Not while I was there he didn't. What's the trouble?'

'What's the bloody trouble?' He looked at his watch. 'About forty minutes ago, at 2040 hrs to be precise, a whole band of those bloody reds arrived here under the command of a Lieutenant in the American Army. Lieutenant Mark was his name.'

I nodded and said, 'Go on.'

'Well, this Lieutenant's loaded with documents all stamped from the Army Commander downwards, ordering everyone to afford him every assistance.'

'So what's the fuss about?'

'What's the bloody fuss about? You may well ask. Only that he marches off the Contessa and her right hand man Antonio.'

Seeing the look of amazement on my face he added, 'I'm sorry, Sir, but there was bugger all any of us could do about it. With all that bumpf he'd got we didn't stand a chance if we'd stood up to him. All we'd have got would have been a load of Court Martials.'

'Didn't he give any reason?'

'How strong are you feeling?' asked Sergeant Jones. He pulled forward a chair into which I sank.

'Yes, he did. I'm sorry, Sir, but it seems that your Contessa and her husband were two of the leading Fascists in Udine.'

'Her husband? But he's missing. She told me he was dead.'

'That's what she told you, Sir. I'm afraid you're not going to like it one little bit, Sir. The fact of the matter is that Antonio was her husband.'

I put my hand to my head and said 'Oh no! I don't believe it.'

'I'm afraid it's the truth, Sir. That's why the partisans have been hanging around the place like flies for the last week. They suspected it was him but couldn't be sure. He'd sprouted a beard and let his hair grow long, and if you recollect he never once went out of the villa. The partisans wanted to get in to have a close look at him, but on your instructions we kept them out.' Seeing that I was genuinely distressed he added: 'I'm sorry, Sir. We're all very sorry. I'm afraid that bitch took you for a right ride.'

I stood up from the chair and told Driver Lane to bring back the fifteen-hundredweight and drive me back to Udine.

It was around midnight when I reached the hotel where Lieutenant Mark had established his headquarters. Outside several partisans, draped with bombs and carrying Tommy guns, lounged. They took no notice of me as I pushed my way past them into the deserted hall. Not quite knowing where Lieutenant Mark's quarters were I ran up the stairs. At the top there were two more guards.

'The Tenente?' I shouted.

They pointed towards a door and laughed.

Without pausing I flung open the door and found myself in an empty room in the centre of which was a large double bed. From the door that led into the bathroom there came the sound of voices and running water.

I crossed the room and looked into the bathroom.

Lieutenant Mark was standing up in the bath and kneeling before him in the water was the Contessa massaging him with foaming soap.

Catching sight of me Mark called out: 'Hi, Mike. Come to join the sport? Strip off and come right on in. She's some dame this one I don't mind telling you.' He leant forward and slapped her across the face. 'Got to work it off haven't you, you bloody little fascist bitch. That's right, keep at it and maybe I won't have your old man put up against a wall and shot, though God knows the bastard deserves it.' He turned to me. 'You're a right one, Mike. I didn't realise your mob was billeted on this cow. If you don't mind me saying so you sure were a bit slow.'

'Is it true?'

'Is what true?'

'The Contessa and her husband were fascists?'

'Not only fascists, Mike my boy, but right bastard fascists into the bargain.' He leant down and hit her across the face. 'You were a fucking fascist whore, weren't you, Contessa?' When she did not reply he hit her again.

She looked up at him and through the steam I saw no tears in her eyes, only hatred. She turned towards me, and still there was no softening in those eyes.

I ran out of the bathroom. Behind me I heard Mark call out: 'Don't you fancy this one. Mike? Hang on a second and I'll have the boys bring on the dancing girls and you can take you pick.'

Although the Contessa did not cry, I was weeping when I reached my fifteen-hundredweight. Driver Lane looked at me strangely, made no comment, and drove me back to the platoon.

Luckily for me a flap blew up the following day. I was not quite sure what it was about, except that it concerned Trieste, to which delightful port Tito was still laying claim. As a result by midday what was left of the Brigade round Udine had struck camp and moved into Trieste to join its other half and the New Zealanders.

My drivers were extremely annoyed. They accepted the discomfort of being perpetually on the move in time of war, but now that the Armistice had been signed, they felt that they were entitled to rest and quiet. I had never before heard so much grumbling, answering back, all verging on mutiny, and in my shocked condition I had to take a firm hold on myself to keep my temper under control. Nor were matters improved by several of my drivers coming up to me and offering their condolences. I don't mean to say that they were taking the mickey out of me. It was just that I didn't want to be reminded of the love that had failed me. I made up my mind not to become emotionally entangled until I was out of the army for good.

Looking back, the squabbling over Trieste was just the beginning of the post-war wrangles that continue to this day. At the time it seemed to me monstrous that one of our former allies should be prepared to cause so much trouble. I had imagined that peace had come to stay. How mistaken I was! It was the same after the war of 1914–1918, in which millions had died to make the world safe. I can remember my father telling me of the sense of relief that swept through the nation on Armistice day. The world had been made safe for democracy. All was well. The League of Nations was established within whose bosom the peoples of the world resolve their differences without taking up arms. When the world fell apart again in 1939 he found it incredible that such a thing could happen so soon after the recent bloodbath.

It was towards evening that I led my platoon into Trieste where I was met by a Corporal from Headquarters on a motor-cycle. He was looking white and bad-tempered.

When I asked him what the trouble was he replied: 'Just you bloody well wait and see.'

He remounted his motor-cycle and we followed him through the main part of the town of Trieste until we reached the outskirts on the far side. Here he turned into the local abattoir and I led my column of trucks in after him.

I saw at once that we were to be all together in this unsavoury area, Headquarters Company, the two platoons and the Workshop Company.

Harry came over to me looking pale around his gills. 'Come and have a slug, you'll need it,' he said. He led the way into one of the offices which was serving as the Officers' Mess and poured me a drink.

'What's the matter? Everyone looks like death,' I said.

'You've hit the nail on the head,' he said. 'This is a camp of death. I'll show you round in a minute.'

'Camp of death?'

'Kind of concentration camp, an Italian one. Just you wait and see. Have another drink; you'll need it.'

At this point Tommy came storming into the hut in a foul temper. 'What the hell Brigade thinks it's up to putting us in this dump is beyond me.' He held out his hand and Harry placed a glass in it, whose contents Tommy swallowed at a gulp. 'We've got to get out of here as soon as possible. The chaps are hopping mad. I don't blame them. This place stinks of death. Even the birds won't sing round here.' He turned to me. 'Listen, Mike, first thing tomorrow have a good scout round and see what you can find for the whole company. The Brigade Major says you have his authority, except you mustn't fall foul of the bloody Jugs who are still in the town in some strength, looting and making a general nuisance of themselves. We're not to get involved with them. According to the B.M. it's a political matter now. The war is over, and the army is once again a pawn in the hands of the politicians with no power to make its own decisions.'

Today we have seen so many pictures and films of man's inhumanity to man that we are no longer moved. We have become accustomed to those skeletons in the concentration camps piled one upon the other. Human skin made into lampshades is old hat. The ever-growing horror of the weapons of war, the constant use of highly developed naplam bombs leaves us cold. Modern communication has dulled our sensibilities, so that I doubt if it is possible today for the majority of us to be shocked. We may say, 'How awful', but our bowels are unmoved.

In Trieste I saw my first concentration camp, and it moved me to a degree to which I have never since been moved. It made me bring up over and over again.

There was the charnel house. The Italians, for this was an Italian camp, had attempted to blow up the ovens in which they burned what was left of the racked remains of their victims. Being in a hurry to destroy the evidence they had made a hash of the job. From beneath the rubble protruded charred heads, arms and legs, over which the flies crawled.

With a perverse sense of humour the slaughter section of the abattoir had been used as the torture centre. Along its walls were the original butchers hooks, and below each one were congealed pools of human blood, which was also splattered over the wall.

What struck me at the time was the vast amount of human shit smeared all over the place. Where there was blood there was shit. The stench was indescribable.

Facing the row of hooks was a line of dog kennels, measuring six feet long by three feet wide and three feet high. Each one of these kennels was thick with human faeces. Somewhat ludicrously lying upturned in front of one of them was a baby's enamel chamber pot. I can still see it to this day, and wonder what possible use it could have been in that Augean stable. It could only have been someone with the most perverted sense of humour who had put it there.

Harry took me by the arm and led me to the end of the row of kennels and pointed. Inside the last kennel, whose rough, barred door was open, two naked figures lay in one another's arms. They must have been dead for several weeks, but I could still see the lacerations on their naked bodies where they had been beaten so hard that the wounds were open to the bones. From what was left of them they were still identifiable as a man and a woman.

None of us was happy that night, nor do I think that many of us slept peacefully. When I wrote that no bird sang in that place, I was writing the truth. Over the whole area there lay an atmosphere of the utmost melancholy such as I have never experienced before or since. It affected us all, from Tommy down to the drivers. Our main feeling was one of disbelief. Of course, we had heard of concentration camps. In our small way we had encountered in our campaigns some of the horrors of war. We had seen men dreadfully wounded, we had seen men die. But somehow the way the unfortunate victims had died in this place of degradation shook us all more than we had been shaken before.

There was no singing in the platoon lines that night. There was a certain amount of drinking in the backs of the waggons, but the voices of the drivers were lowered as they recounted to each other the beastliness they had just seen, and wondered how on earth man could behave in such a way.

For my part I did not sleep at all that night. Driver Lane had fixed me up a bed in the back of my fifteen-hundredweight, but I had no inclination to lie down. First of all it seemed indecent to sleep in such a place where I could still feel the pain all round me. Added to which there was perpetually in my nostrils the reek of that torture chamber, a mixture of human excrement, decaying flesh and blood. This was not imagination on my part. Several days later I talked with my drivers about it, and they all agreed that the stench in that place was so unbearable as to make sleep out of the question.

I was standing outside my truck feeling utterly depressed at about four in the morning when the Corporal Cook came up and gave me a cup of tea.

'Think we ought to get to hell out of here as soon as possible before we all go round the bloody bend,' he said. 'Do you know, Sir, I had to give all last night's grub away to the Eyties? The lads couldn't look a soya link in the face.'

I sent Driver Lane to tell Sergeant Jones to report to me with a three-tonner, Corporal and half-a-dozen men. I had made up my mind not to spend another night in that hell on earth. If I couldn't find a better location for the company by the end of the day I was not worthy of the two pips that His Majesty had seen fit to place on my shoulder.

Half an hour later we were out of the abattoir with Sergeant Jones at the wheel and me beside him and a squad of determined drivers in the back.

Straightaway I realized that the choice locations along the sea front were out of the question. The New Zealanders were there in force. General Freyberg V.C. had established his Headquarters in the Villa Miramar the one-time home of the ill-fated Maximilian, Emperor of Mexico. The centre of the town was no better. The Armoured Brigade was squeezed in between the Jugs who still seemed to have all the best hotels and houses under their control.

After an hour's fruitless search I realized that it was hopeless to continue to look in what the estate agents would term the prime positions. There was nothing for it but to settle for something less smart in the suburbs. Accordingly I told Sergeant Jones to steer for the out-skirts of Trieste.

Here things were no better. The Jugs were even thicker on the ground, and hostile into the bargain, so that my squad in the back of the truck became anxious. They pointed out that they had survived the hazards and the dangers of the war; that it would be most inconsiderate of me to lead them into a situation where they might suffer serious injury or even death at the hands of roving bands of ruffians, even if technically they were still our allies.

I was in complete agreement with these sentiments. I had just in-structed Sergeant Jones to about turn and make for home, wondering as I did so how I could face Tommy's displeasure at the failure of my mission when we happened to pass a magnificent Palladian Villa, standing in vast grounds of its own, surrounded by a substantial wall. Its impos-ing gates were somewhat the worse for wear. Their stone escutcheons had been used for target practice by the brave members of the Yugoslav Republic People's Army who had also amused themselves by indis-crimately peppering the villa itself, no doubt to express their displeasure with the capitalist system.

My heart missed a beat. There was only one Jug guarding the entrance. Admittedly he was draped with the usual fancy dress, grenades and automatic weapons of all nations. Still, he was alone. We were eight and desperate into the bargain.

I instructed Sergeant Jones to swing the lorry round and stop opposite the entrance to this magnificent prize.

Having instructed two of my drivers to give me covering fire if necessary, and having ordered the other four on no account to attempt it knowing that it would mean my certain death, I swung myself down from the cab and approached the guard.

As I drew near he reacted violently and pointed what looked very much like a Russian sten gun in my direction which occasioned Sergeant Jones, who was just behind me, to remark, 'Careful, Sir. The silly bugger probably doesn't know how it works and it might go off by mistake.'

I stopped, not wishing to make that particular piece of ground forever England. I would have given up then and there, knowing that the drivers who were watching me would have disapproved of my placing my life in jeopardy and would not for one moment have considered retreat to be in any way cowardly, but the guard grinned at me and muttered, '*Sigaretta, sigaretta.*' I put my hand in my pocket and pulled out a full packet of English cigarettes. The effect was amazing. The guard dropped his sten and, with the rest of his armaments clanking loudly, ran towards me, snatched the packet from my hands, tore it open, crammed a handful into his mouth and began to chew them. As he did so a look of ecstasy suffused his unshaven features. Having slaked his craving for nicotine he pointed to his throat, indicating that he was in need of some form of liquid nourishment.

My drivers had been watching the performance with lewd cries of encouragement. Now one of them leapt down from the back of the truck, opened the tool box, and took out a bottle of Scotch which he brought forward and offered to the guard, who opened it, sniffed it suspiciously, then took a swig. Clearly it was to his liking. He took another swig, and muttered: 'Buono, bello.' He picked up his sten gun and thumped on the gates.

Immediately the imposing portals were opened and an even more ruffianly looking brigand, loaded down with the accoutrements of war, walked out and joined his companion who handed him the bottle of Scotch.

Soon they were jabbering away in a foreign tongue which one of my drivers declared to be Jugoslavian. Whatever it was, one thing was certain, the lower the whisky sank in the bottle, the faster they talked, and the higher my spirits rose.

'The question is, are there any more of the buggers inside,' said Sergeant Jones.

Seeing as I was prepared to endanger my life just now on all your behalf, Sergeant,' I said, 'I now order you when we have got these two brigands totally and utterly pissed, to slip past them, enter the house, carry out a full but careful reconnaissance and report back to me with all possible speed.'

At this point the two guards, who had by now consumed my packet of cigarettes and drunk the whisky, were demanding more. Clearly they regarded me as a cornucopia fallen from the skies.

I turned to my drivers. 'More whisky,' I commanded.

This order was met by a disappointing response.

'Got plenty of grappa, Sir. Whisky's like gold. Can't see why we should waste it on these sods.'

'So you want to remain in the concentration camp do you?' I said sarcastically. 'Listen to me. This is not a request. It's an order. I want more whisky.'

One of the drivers sullenly produced a second bottle from the bowels of the lorry. 'All right, Sir. But I want a written guarantee that you'll replace it.'

When I had taken the bottle I said: 'Listen to me, driver. You will receive no written guarantee. But I can promise you one thing.'

'What's that, Sir?'

'Your reward shall be in Heaven, driver.'

I handed the whisky over to the two guards along with another packet of cigarettes in case they might still feel hungry. Not wishing to seem unsociable I told Driver Lane to bring me a glass in order that I should not fail in my duty to cement the Jugoslav-Brittanic Entente Cordiale. I regret to say that this move on my part was greeted by some offensive remarks from my drivers who were still standing round the truck very much in the background.

I turned round and said, 'That's quite enough unless you all want to be up on a charge.'

'Oh come off your bloody horse, Sir,' they chorused adding other obscenities.

'I merely wish to point out that should you find yourself occupying these high class quarters tonight, it will be me alone you will have to thank. Kindly bear that in mind. I placed my life in danger for the greater good . . . the summum bonum.'

The whisky had gone to my head.

'Mr Nelson's gone raving bonkers again,' said one of the drivers.

'One day he'll go too bloody far and they'll come and take him away in a plain van,' said another.

Further ribaldry was interrupted by the reappearance of Sergeant Jones. He looked excited. He beckoned me to come inside the gates.

Calculating that the guards were now almost at the doors of oblivion, I left them and joined him inside.

'Meet the Duke,' said Sergeant Jones.

'Ah Lieutenant, I am so glad you have come. Welcome to my home,' said a small man with greying hair, wearing an impeccable Savile Row suit.

Before I could prevent him he had thrown his arms around me and was embracing me on both cheeks as the tears poured down his face.

'We'd better get a move on, Sir, if you don't mind breaking up the happy party,' said Sergeant Jones. 'The Duke, at least he says he's a Duke, an Austrian Duke for some reason which you no doubt with your superior education will be able to figure out, says there are usually a band of twenty to thirty Jugs here. They left this morning for Gorizia where they are being addressed by Tito and some other big wigs. They're expected back tonight.'

'Lieutenant, I implore you to move your men in here at once. Everything I have is yours, or rather what I have left,' interrupted the Duke. 'Your Sergeant is right. I am an Austrian Duke of the Hapsburg Empire. My family has lived here many years. But these terrible Jugoslavs are destroying everything, everything, just for the sake of destruction. It is terrible what they have done here. They have slashed my pictures with knives, shot at my statues with their pistols, and made a public lavatory of every room in the place. Please, please, move your men in I beg of you. I have many influential friends in England and I promise you your kindness shall not go unrewarded.'

I turned to Sergeant Jones, 'Right, Sergeant. Your map. What is the map reference?'

'I suggest, Sir, you forget the map reference. If you remember the last one you wrote down resulted in five unfortunate drivers going into the bag.'

'At a time like this I think it unkind of you to remind me of that unfortunate error.'

'I merely thought, Sir, that it would be expedient to avoid a similar occurrence.'

At that moment one of the drivers came up to me and said: 'The two guards are flat out, Sir.'

'Are you sure?'

'Don't be so bloody daft, Sir. I know a drunk when I see one. I should have thought you would have known that by now, Sir.'

'Don't be impertinent,' I said. 'Right, Sergeant. Bring the two bodies and the rest of the men inside. You will proceed with all possible speed back to Headquarters. Acquaint Major Thompson with the situation, and impress upon him that speed is essential. I would suggest that you rustle up all the men and trucks that are not out on duty and come back straight away. We need reinforcements more than anything else. If the

Boys anti-tank gun can be found, together with any ammunition and anyone brave enough to fire it, bring them along. Also the bren guns, preferably with their mags loaded with tracer. I will remain here and hold the fort. But Sergeant, remember I am heavily outnumbered. There is a limit to what I and this handful of brave drivers can do. Dismiss.'

Sergeant Jones was so impressed by this speech, which must go down in the annals of history with the one delivered on the eve of Thermopylae, that he even saluted before turning and hurrying out of the gates.

I heard the engine of the three-tonner start up, and the next minute it was roaring away in the direction of the main part of the town.

Having ordered the drivers who had remained with me to close the gates behind them and on no account to make any noise, I allowed the Duke to take me on a conducted tour of the house.

I could see at once that it would be an absolutely ideal location for the entire company. The house itself must have had about fifty rooms, more than enough to put all the men under cover. The grounds were just of a size to accommodate the company's vehicles, and I earmarked the stables for the workshop section.

A considerable amount of damage had been inflicted everywhere by the comrades. Priceless Empire furniture had been wantonly smashed and scattered all over the place. One might have forgiven this had it been chopped up for fuel to keep the children of the revolution warm. But the weather was spring-like. Nearly every picture in the place had been slashed with knives, or peppered with bullets; the chandeliers had been the object of target practice. What I found particularly strange was that although the villa was adequately equipped with lavatories in working order, the comrades had shown preference for the staircases and the corners of the main salons. I could only assume that these acts of defecation must have expressed in some way their disapproval of the capitalist system.

The Duke, in spite of everything, was in good spirits. Every now and again as he conducted me round his villa, which seemed more like a palace to me, he would stop to embrace me and thank me for coming to his rescue. Over and over again he made me promise that I would stay; that on no account would I go away and leave him to what he called the mercies of the barbarians. Apologizing for the state of the place he promised that he would set his family to work to clean it up and make it fit for English officers and gentlemen.

After the conducted tour, during which I had determined to keep the main State Room for my personal use, judging that Tommy would not deny it me after my magnificent discovery, which could do nothing but raise the morale of the entire company, the Duke conducted me down to the cellar to meet his family.

Here he introduced me to his wife and three daughters. They all looked haggard, but after the Duke had harangued them in German for several minutes they cheered up, threw their arms around me and embraced me vigorously.

I am glad to say that none of them could compare with the Contessa in beauty, and my heart was not moved. I had no desire to make a fool of myself a second time.

When I suggested to the Duke that the first thing to do was to move himself and his family out of the cellars to which they had been condemned by the Jugs, he would not hear of it. I persisted, and we finally came to an arrangement whereby he and his family and those of his staff who had stayed behind would occupy a wing of the stables.

Naturally I was very anxious for news of the rest of the company and I was greatly relieved when Driver Lane joined us to inform me that Sergeant Jones was already back with a fighting advance party of the company; that Major Thompson sent me his congratulations and was recommending me for a high award. Having sent Driver Lane away with amessage to Sergeant Jones to post guards and mount brens around the perimeter and to cover the main gate with the Boys anti-tank, I retired with the Duke to his private study.

Here the scene of desolation was complete. The thousands of books with which the walls were lined had been thrown onto the floor. Many of them had been torn apart. In one corner of the room someone had tried to start a bonfire with the tomes which he must have found particularly offensive.

Against one wall a safe stood with its doors loose on its hinges. Clearly someone had managed to blast it open with a grenade or two.

Seeing my look of condolence the Duke smiled: 'Have no fear, the barbarians can see no further than their eyes.'

He crossed the room and, putting his hands to the wall, pressed. A wide section of the wall swung back revealing a second safe. He took a key from his pocket, unlocked it and opened the heavy door. I looked over his shoulder and saw that it was stacked with documents and small bags that clearly contained coins. He disregarded these, bent down, and lifted up a bottle of champagne.

'The Krug '96,' he remarked. 'My last bottle, my dear Lieutenant, but there will never be a day as worthy of it.'

From that moment I started to grow very fond of the Duke. I greatly admired his stoicism. In his adversity not once did he complain. In the days to come, when we often would talk till the early hours of the morning, not once did he try to make excuses for his own side. By training an historian, he was interested in facts, not emotions. To this day I can still see his tapering fingers pointing towards me and hear his slightly guttural voice admonishing me, 'Ah, but my dear Lieutenant, you are a poet and a dreamer, and the realities of logic have no interest for you.'

In 1955 I was in Venice on an assignment for a television company, and having some time in hand I drove up to Trieste to call upon him. He had aged considerably. His innate gentleness was unaltered. His wife had died and his daughters were married. Yet he did not seem a lonely man. We talked far into the night about the old days, and he told me that on the very day I had arrived at his villa, he and his family had spent the whole of the previous night in prayer. I had not known it at the time, but it was almost certain that if the rest of the Jugoslavs who were occupying his villa had returned that night, they would have come with orders to shoot him and his entire family.

The Duke was greatly disappointed about one small matter. He had written to his 'cousin', the King of England, recommending me for my bravery, and it had been a bitter blow to him that His Majesty, although he had acknowledged his communication, had not seen fit to elevate me to the Order of the Garter. Personally I would have settled for a knighthood. It would have made reservations in restaurants so much easier.

By six o'clock that evening nearly the entire company was safely behind the Duke's walls. All weak spots had been repaired and those that could not be were covered by brens. Towards sunset the entire camp stood to alert, but there was no sign of the enemy. The Jugs finally put in an appearance towards midnight and, finding the main gates barred to them, started to let loose with everything they'd got. They even had the audacity to lob a couple of grenades over the wall. This proved too much for the Company Sergeant Major, who had been disturbed from his sleep, having retired early to bed considerably the worse for wear. Seizing a bren he climbed on top of the wall and proceeded to loose off several magazines of tracer in the direction of the perpetrators of this unfriendly action. Not content with this he ordered the Quartermaster, an ex-infanteer and accordingly well versed in offensive weapons, to put down a few rounds of 2″ mortar to show the enemy that we were not to be trifled with. I am still not sure why we were in possession of such a dangerous weapon as a 2″ mortar. I am quite certain it was not part of our official equipment.

This practical exposition of the Churchillian spirit, which would have delighted the old man himself, was greeted with cheers by members of all ranks who were no doubt reminded of November the Fifth in the days of peace. Some of them, feeling that the C.S.M.'s lead entitled them to follow suit, loosed off their rifles into the direction of the enemy. But the majority were content to watch the display, reasoning that if a rifle was fired the bloody thing would have to be cleaned.

Major Thompson was delighted with what he called my display of initiative far beyond the call of normal duty and, like the Duke, felt that I should not go unrewarded. He promised that I should be sent on leave to England at the earliest opportunity. To show his immediate appreciation he commanded that I should be relieved of all duties and direct my obvious abilities to making him and my fellow officers as comfortable as possible. In other words I became a kind of hotel manager.

I had never been very impressed with the standard of catering in Tommy's mess. I had no complaints about the drink. Provided one liked gin, one was well cared for. The food was a very different kettle of fish. So a few days after we had moved in, I went to the Duke and laid my problem before him. Like the gentleman he was he insisted that I should avail myself of the services of his number one chef, Giorgio, late of the Ritz in Madrid and the Danieli in Venice, and entered into the spirit of the game.

Our immediate problem was to secure the basic materials with which Giorgio could practise his art. We had plenty of tea, bully beef, soya links masquerading as sausages, spam which we had secured from the Americans, tinned milk, tinned margarine which we sometimes used in the rear axles of our trucks, and flour. But we were desperately short of meat, eggs and fresh vegetables.

There was nothing to do but to enter the black market. Never before nor since have I seen a Duke, distantly related to the House of Hapsburg, throw himself into the game with such abandon and relish. For the first time the Duke was breaking the law, and he enjoyed every second of it.

Money was not of great use, so every morning we loaded tea, margarine and bully beef into the back of a three-tonner along with several cartons of cigarettes with which to trade. You might say the former represented the silver element in the world of barter; the cigarettes were the gold and were only produced when all else failed.

I would drive the truck with Giorgio wedged between me and the Duke who spent most of the time waving out of the window shouting greetings at all and sundry, many of whom could scarcely conceal their surprise to see so august and revered a figure thundering by in a truck belonging to the British Army. In the back rode Driver Lane armed with a pickaxe to repel boarders.

Our first call would be the port. Here we would pick up strange Mediterranean fish, large prawns, and the occasional lobster. To begin with I would do the bargaining, while the Duke acted as interpreter. But it didn't take me long to realize that his innate cunning was greater than mine. It had been lying dormant for many years, and now it blossomed out like a flower in spring.

I must say that the Duke was a real tryer. He hated to give up until he had run his quarry to ground. As he seemed to know everyone of consequence in Trieste, he was constantly being given useful leads. It was rumoured that so and so had killed a few pigs; there was a crop of tomatoes at such and such a farm; a couple of calves which had escaped the thieving fingers of the Jugs were about to be slaughtered; a certain wine shop was said to be selling some good Orvieto and Barolo which had just been dug up. Off we would go, following up each of these clues and more often than not success would crown our efforts.

After a particularly fine coup the Duke would insist on celebrating, and take me to the houses of his smart friends who would open a bottle or two of their finest wines, while he boasted to them of his prowess on the Black Market. Up till then he had clearly been pursuing the wrong career.

Although the finest delicacies found their way to the Officers' Mess after passing through Giorgio's magical hands, I had not forgotten my lessons on Man Management instilled into me in the days of O.C.T.U. long ago. With the Duke's assistance I was able to ensure that a plentiful supply of fresh fruit and vegetables, the odd carcase or two, and fish on Fridays, found its way into the mens' mess.

Naturally news of the Lucullan feasts at the Duke's villa soon reached the other units of the Brigade, and it was extraordinary the number of officers from the smart tank regiments who often seemed to find themselves in our vicinity at the hour when the sun sank over the yardarm. Tommy made them all welcome. His finest hour dawned when the entire Brigade Headquarters Staff came to dine with us. I can remember the Menu to this day.

> Asparagus Vinaigrette
> Devilled Whitebait
> Noisettes de Veau au Printemps
> Roast Quail with Vegetables Various
> Cheeses
> Wild Strawberries and Cream

The wines.

> Champagne Veuve Cliquot '21 from the
> cellar of the Duke
> Barolo '39
> Port, shippers and vintage unknown from
> the cellar of the Duke
> Brandy, very Old French, from the cellar
> of the Duke

Studying that menu today I do not think it is at all bad but I am still slightly unhappy about mixing French and English.

I am pleased too to see that even at that tender age I had the sense to put the cheese before the wild strawberries. I am convinced that this is the correct order. Cheese leaves a cloying taste in the mouth. Wild strawberries enable one to finish the meal with a delicacy on the breath that will not offend one's best friend.

I knew that this halcyon existence could not continue much longer. For the first time in the role of manager of a first class hotel I had found my niche.

A few days after the Brigadier had dined with us I happened to be in the kitchen mulling over with Giorgio further culinary delights, when I received a message to report at once to Major Thompson's office.

I knocked on his door, entered and saluted. I noticed that he was looking white.

'Anything the matter, Sir?'

He pointed to a chair. 'You'd better sit down, Michael,' he said. He held out a piece of paper. As I read it my eyes blurred, but the gist of the message was horribly clear.

Lieutenant Nelson was instructed to report to 'X' Transport Company on the beaches of Salerno, where he would undergo training on Amphibious Vehicles with a view to engaging the Japanese in the Far East in deadly combat.

I suppose I should have felt proud that my country still needed experienced officers like myself to carry the war into the Eastern Camp now that we had vanquished our enemies in Europe. I fear I had no sense of pride.

Looking back I think it was tactless of Tommy to remark sadly, 'God knows who will take over the messing when you've gone, Michael. It will never never be the same again.'

Chapter Five

To be honest, the thought of the Japs did not perturb me unduly. If I had to remain in the army I reckoned it would be better to serve in a zone of activity rather than in peace-torn Europe where, as I have mentioned, the bull already was beginning to rear its head.

My journey south to Salerno was saddened by the absence of Driver Lane. Much as we had enjoyed soldiering together it was clear he had no desire to engage the Japs alongside me. Indeed he went so far as to suggest that the war in the Far East would be brought to a speedier conclusion if those in authority would have the good sense not to send me there. It was with heavy hearts on both sides that we parted company. He had joined me as a batman at Christmas, 1941, and ever since then had followed my ignominious career with an unswerving loyalty. We understood one another. In return for minor services, such as carting my tons of home comforts throughout the Middle East and up the spine of Italy, I guaranteed that he would not perform one more unpleasant duty that was absolutely vital. For Driver Lane there were no guard duties, no pickets, and no standing in cookhouse queues. Like all batmen he was above the reproaches of N.C.O.'s and C.S.M.'s.

When the time came for the parting of our ways, Driver Lane showed a charming solicitude for my financial well-being. Throughout our travels he had always acted as my banker. It might be more correct to say as my private mint. I never asked him where the money came from, but Driver Lane's bank was always well-stocked. Sometimes, when I read in the papers of the complete muddle confronting the currencies of all nations, I am tempted to write a letter to *The Times* suggesting they send for Driver Lane. The world is full of wasted talent.

Over the last three years Driver Lane had taken care of all my gambling debts. I am the world's worst gambler, but I am glad that my losses had benefited my fellow officers, particularly Captain John Fish, who alone among my acquaintances had discovered some loophole whereby he managed to ship vast sums back to the Old Country. This accumulating nest egg was eventually the basis of the successful business which he established after the war. Being of vivid imagination, I sometimes fool myself that I have shares in it.

It is surprising that the British Forces in the Middle East and Italy did not suffer from a severe dose of inflation, because there was far too much money chasing far too few goods. Goods did not include members of the opposite sex, who were obtainable mainly by barter. Although the men had plenty of cash in their pockets, most of them had found no way of remitting it to the United Kingdom. Originally this had been permitted, but unfortunately they overreached themselves and their greed led to their fall.

When I was in Iraq in late 1942 it was still possible to buy Postal Orders from the field Post Office and send them back to Britain. Thousands, possibly millions, of pounds of good money went winging its way to the U.K., until there were no Postal Orders left. This led to an investigation. It was quickly discovered that the weekly pay entitlement of the entire Brigade was being remitted to the U.K. at least twenty times over. In other words a great number of soldiers were on the fiddle with the Wogs, selling them army equipment, both surplus and vital, and sending the proceeds back to their loved ones. That was the end of that racket.

Driver Lane was determined that I should be comfortable if not happy on my journey to Salerno. On no account did he want me to put up for the nights at transit camps or other such military centres. Army rations were out of the question and as far as he was concerned only the best was good enough for me. I was to stay at the grandest hotels, eat at the best restaurants, and if I felt like dalliance I was only to dally with the fairest that the country could offer. Accordingly he handed me over the small attaché case which had accompanied him on all our wanderings.

It was not a very strong case, and over the years had become jagged at the edges and difficult to close. I think the difficulty in securing it was probably more due to the fact that it was always heavily overloaded with the currencies of all nations, rather than to any slipshod work on the part of its manufacturers. I had developed a great affection for this dowdy object. Many were the mornings when I had been woken by Driver Lane offering me a cup of sweet tea into which he had prudently slipped several fingers of brandy. As soon as I had taken a few reviving sips and started my heart he would produce the case and remark: 'Well, how much do you need this time? The Mess Corporal tells me you made a right prick of yourself at poker last night.'

I can hardly be blamed for falling in love with this Pandora's box. When Driver Lane presented it to me before my departure, tied about with cord and containing an abundance of lire and reserve currencies, I knew that there was no greater gift he could give me. I appreciated what a wrench it must be for him to part with it, and I hope he knew that I appreciated this act of friendship.

'I wouldn't be surprised if you get through the bloody lot before you reach Salerno,' he commented. 'I suppose you'll have it away with those posh bints of yours in Rome. Just take care you don't get the pox. There's always a first time remember. I suppose you'll be staying at that thieving Albergo Grande.'

'I shouldn't be surprised. If you're feeling fatherly, let me remind you, Driver Lane, that you've had more than your share of the other in our wanderings.'

'Anyway,' he continued, 'I've put an emergency reserve in the back of your fifteen-hundredweight and I've told Driver Tibbs where to cash it in on the way down.'

Driver Tibbs was another unfortunate who found himself in the unhappy position of having to proceed to the Far East. Personally I had my doubts. I had a suspicion that they would have to shackle him in chains to get him East of Suez.

The weather was set fair. I had plenty of money. Driver Tibbs was a lively companion, yet it was not a happy journey. I fell into a state of melancholy. It was as if I was back at the beginning of my army career, back at Inkermann barracks learning how to survive as a driver. It seemed to me that I had lost all my friends, Major Tommy, Harry, Driver Lane, Sergeant Jones, and Corporal Johnson, whose clap I hope was reacting favourably to the new wonder drug called penicillin. I fooled myself that the days in Iraq with John Fish, our crawl up Italy, our adventures on the Anzio beachhead, had been happy ones. I even imagined that I missed the benevolent if firm guidance of Major Hawkins.

The first night I stopped at Venice. The splendours of a suite at the Danieli failed to cheer me. Was it really only a few weeks ago since I had liberated Venice with Captain Fish? It all seemed long long ago.

At Ravenna I decided that a dose of culture was what I needed. But the dazzling mosaics of the Mausoleum of Galla Placidia could not rouse me from my gloom; the octagonal Basilica of San Vitale, one of the most remarkable buildings in the world, with its rich marbles and fantastic mosaics, left me cold. I stood before the tomb of Dante and felt even more depressed. This may have been due to the fact that I have always found him unreadable.

South of Rimini I turned inland and visited the town of Morciano. Looking across the rows of crosses in the Allied war cemetry I could not help remembering with some bitterness that it was here many months ago that the race to Vienna was to have started, a race that never got beyond the foothills on the far side of the town. For one moment I thought of crossing to the other side of Italy to revisit the battlefields of Anzio where Captain Fish had so narrowly escaped death at my hands, but I decided that all this nostalgia was doing me no good, so I ordered Driver Tibbs to make straight for the Albergo Grande and the fleshpots of the Eternal City.

Although I was not sure what Driver Lane had put into the back of the fifteen-hundredweight as reserve currency, I thought it wisest to get rid of it and to convert it into cash as quickly as possible. Although we had only been stopped once on our way south by some inquisitive members of the Military Police, and they had been satisfied with the movement order supplied to me by Brigade, I feared that the next lot might not be so lenient. They might have the impertinence to look into the back of the truck, and I knew that whatever was there would not reflect to my credit.

As soon as we entered Rome I told Driver Tibbs to go direct to an address which Driver Lane had written on a piece of paper. After making several enquiries we made our way to the Ponte Palatino which we crossed and found ourselves in the Trastevere, an old quarter of the city crisscrossed with narrow streets filled with villainous looking Romans. Smelling the drains Driver Tibbs remarked that the greatest mistake the Allies ever made was not to bomb Rome.

Finally we came to a halt in a cul-de-sac in front of some gates which must have been original fifteenth century, and have no doubt long since been borne away in triumph by some antique dealer. Our vehicle was immediately surrounded by about twenty to thirty children aged anything from five to fifteen, some of whom clamoured for cigarettes, while the rest circled the truck looking for any possible weak spot where they might effect an entry. Both Driver Tibbs and I were well versed in these juvenile tactics and while he guarded the rear I took up my position in the front. Having called to a likely looking lad and bribed him with a packet of cigarettes, he disappeared through a small entrance in the gates, and reappeared in a few minutes with a well-dressed young man of about twenty who shook hands and welcomed me to Rome. I introduced him to Driver Tibbs and soon they were chatting away like old friends.

'If you'll wait out here, Sir,' said Driver Tibbs after they had concluded the preliminary parley, 'I will go inside and complete the transaction.'

It had always been understood that, holding the King's Commission, I must never soil my hands with trade.

Accordingly, while I stood outside the gates surrounded by an ever growing crowd of adolescents, expecting to be torn apart any minute,

Driver Tibbs drove the truck through the gates and disappeared from view.

I was growing increasingly anxious as the children swarmed around me, doing their best to lift my pistol from its holster, undo my braces and remove my trousers, when to my great relief the young man and Driver Tibbs drove out.

The young man got out, we shook hands, I climbed in and with a wave of my hand we drove off in the direction of the Albergo Grande. I noticed that Driver Tibbs was sweating.

'Anything the matter?' I asked.

'Fuck me,' was all he could reply.

'I beg your pardon.'

Driver Tibbs swore again.

'Do you think you ought to stop and have a drink of water?'

'That bloody Driver Lane of yours has done you proud.' He pointed to a brown paper parcel about eight inches by six lying on the seat between us.

I knew it was bad form for me to ask the actual figure of the day's takings. Had I done so with Driver Lane, he would have given me a stony stare and replied: 'There are some things it's best for officers not to enquire about.' As to what had been bartered I never dared to put the question.

But Driver Tibbs was new to the game. It was his first engagement as a batman. We were two unfortunate soldiers thrown together by the hazards of war on our way south through Italy to the Far East. I hadn't the slightest doubt that at that very moment he was wondering what kind of an officer I was and what his cut would be.

'How much?' I asked.

'Two thousand quid's worth, give or take a few lire.'

'Let's stop at the first hostelry and drink a bottle of the best to Driver Lane,' I said.

At that moment as we were passing a café, Driver Tibbs drew the truck alongside one of the tables that had been put out on the pavement. We got out and sat down on a couple of chairs, positioning ourselves in such a way that the truck was under our observation. I had no desire to find it suddenly short of a couple of tyres, a radiator and back axle. The Romans were in the fourth division of thieving compared with the Wogs and the Neapolitans, and were no match for veterans like Driver Tibbs and myself, but a modicum of vigilance was still called for.

Feeling in a generous mood I summoned the daughter of the family and ordered the best dry white wine of the establishment, which turned

out to be a crisp and drinkable Frascati. I say daughter of the family'
because again veterans like Driver Tibbs and myself had become
knowledgeable about the way Italian cafes and bistros were run, in the
course of our progress northwards through the country. Mother did the
cooking, the daughter or daughters waited and did the cleaning and
washing up, while the male members of the family loafed about the
place, drank and played cards and kept an eye on the daughters to
ensure that they got up to no hanky panky with the allied soldiery. This
was probably why our soldiers developed a hatred for the Italian
men.

When we had drunk the first bottle and ordered a second I said:
'Driver Tibbs, I don't want you to get the wrong idea and think that I
am generous by nature. I am not. However, I have more than enough
cash at the moment, in fact more than I care to carry on me. Accordingly
we will divide that bundle in half.'

'Do you mean it, Sir?'

'On one condition. Tell me what it was you flogged just now.'

'*Gomme*. A load of bloody *gomme*, Sir.'

When I heard this word I was filled with an even greater admiration
for Driver Lane, and once again could not help feeling sad at having lost
his services forever. For gomme was the magic word at that time which
was on every driver's lips and haunted him in his dreams. Rubber in the
form of tyres was even more valuable in Italy than cigarettes. Rubber
could make a driver richer than Croesus. As Italy slowly reverted to
peace, transport was the number one priority. The railroads would take
several months to function properly and, meanwhile, transport on the
roads was urgently required. A man with a lorry that was mobile could
make himself a fortune. Lorries needed tyres. And tyres just did not
exist outside the Army depots whose staff guarded them even more
keenly than Italian fathers guarded their daughters' virginity. The
shortage was to last for about a year until American Lease Lend started
to pour into the conquered countries straight into the hands of the Black
Marketeers and the Mafia. In the same way as many a fortune in England
was founded on the miseries of the Nineteenth Century Industrial
Revolution, so vast wealth was accumulated by a criminal element in
Italy between 1945 and 1950. Today the second generation of this
post-war phenomenon are busy hanging Picassos on their walls, educat-
ing the third generation in Switzerland, or sending them to Eton, taking
good care to refer to grandpa as a successful industrialist who did a great
deal to help in the reconstruction of Italy after the unfortunate war
into which Mussolini plunged the country.

'Where are you going to stay for the next couple of days in Rome?' I asked Driver Tibbs. 'Do you want me to get you in at the Grande?'

'No thank you, Sir. I'm fixed up.' He drew a piece of grubby paper from the pocket of his battle-dress blouse. 'Goes by the name of Maria. They all bloody well do. You'd think there wasn't another name in the whole of this blasted country.'

'A company bit?' I asked.

Driver Tibbs nodded.

It was a practice for some drivers to spend their leaves shacked up with a girl. They would live together as man and wife, she would cook for him, he would take her out to restaurants, cafes and the cinema, and naturally they would end the day sleeping together. Being generous by nature it had become the custom for drivers to pass on the name of a particularly charming companion to the fellow members of the company. This seemed to me highly commendable. The drivers knew excatly how much they would have to pay for the girl's company; they would know she was not a gold digger, because if she was she would be struck off the list; she would have to come up to a certain standard of beauty or else she would not have got on the list; and apart from the odd instance she was guaranteed to be clean. The system saved time and money. The drivers didn't have to worry about making a chance selection from the thousands of prostitutes that hung around all the large cities, and like all prostitutes the Italian ones were only interested in one thing, money. It was generally agreed that there was nothing to touch an enthusiastic amateur.

'By the way, Sir, how are you fixed?' asked Driver Tibbs.

'In what way?'

'Bint, Sir. I'm sure you're all right, Sir, because you've always done yourself proud. I mean to say, Sir, that business in Venice was really something. Was it true what the lads said about you? Twenty bits of stuff in a bed all together. That must have been a bit of all right. I hope you'll forgive me asking, but Driver Lane said I was to make sure you were set up.'

'As a matter of fact I'm not.' I said.

Driver Tibbs took another piece of paper out of his pocket and passed it across the table to me. On it was written a telephone number.

'Driver Lane says to tell you she's blonde and a right smasher. He also said to tell you . . .' Here Driver Tibbs hesitated.

'Yes, Driver?'

'To tell you, Sir, that she'll probably kill you but he thinks it's the kind of death you'd enjoy.'

'The cheeky sod,' I said, once again thinking how much I missed Driver Lane.

Half-an-hour later Driver Tibbs deposited me at the entrace to the Grande and drove off with instructions to report back with the truck in forty-eight hours. So far I had been four days travelling south to Naples. I had not been ordered to report to the Company on the beaches at Salerno on a particular date and I reckoned that the war in the Far East could wait for another couple of days.

The Grande was crammed as usual. Officially it was out of bounds to British troops and only those of General rank could be found there together with an increasing number of Italian millionaires who had grown fat on the profits of the war and the Black Market.

The receptionist, who by now knew me well, sadly shook his head as I sauntered up to the desk, and informed me that alas (but) the hotel was full. Whereupon I went through the usual routine of discreetly passing a couple of notes of the largest denomination into his waiting hand. These secured me a room under the eaves. A further financial transaction ensued, and I was given one of the best suites comprising a large bedroom with a four poster, a sitting room, and spacious bathroom.

I have never been averse to bribery or tipping. It was in the course of my army career that I came to appreciate its value. No doubt it is morally wrong, and you can refuse to play the game. If you do so it is at your own risk, and you must not be upset if nothing but discomfort comes your way. It seems to me that in this world one cannot expect something for nothing. A great number of people want the best, and there is not enough of the best to go round. The law of economics is an universal law and there are no exceptions to it. Accordingly the best will always go to the highest bidder.

When one scatters bribes liberally in all directions, one must not fool oneself that one is buying love or respect. One is simply buying a service. In my opinion money spent in this way, as in reconnaissance, is seldom wasted. I have made a point of carrying this habit learned in the army over into civilian life. One doesn't always have to distribute vast sums. Take for instance a simple problem like parking one's car. Say you work for a company which like all companies has a limited number of car parking spaces for its employees. This means that some people will have to go without spaces. It is a very inexpensive matter to ensure that you are not numbered among them. A bottle of Scotch and gin presented to the car park attendants at Christmas or any other time of the year for that matter, will work wonders. There will always be room for you. It is amazing how many people either do not know about this or are too mean to invest a fiver in a couple of bottles, and spend the rest of the year moaning and wondering why they do not receive favourable treatment.

Socialists affirm that tipping is one of the inherent evils in capitalism. A few years ago it was my misfortune to spend a month behind the Iron Curtain in Roumania. Considering that the country is closely joined with bonds of brotherly love to the Soviet Union, I was disappointed on ordering caviare to be presented with the inferior red Manchurian stuff. It was doubly annoying because on all sides in the restaurant I could see the better off comrades guzzling the real stuff by the pound. Then the penny dropped. On entering the restaurant that evening I held in the palm of my hand notes of the national currency to the equivalent of about ten pounds sterling in value. As the head waiter conducted me to my table, the notes were expertly conveyed from my palm to his. This work of a second produced black caviare that night and for breakfast the following morning, lunch and tea, until in spite of prodigious doses of prophylactic vodka my stomach shrieked for mercy.

I should warn beginners that there is considerable art in the passing of money. It should never be done openly in such a way that it can be perceived by other members of the public clamouring for caviare, a suite in a hotel, or merely a table in an overcrowded restaurant. The notes must be exchanged unobserved and gracefully. The hands of the giver and the receiver should only brush; there should be no harsh contact, just the lightest touch of fairy wings. There must be no change of expression on the face of the giver or the receiver. The whole transaction must be delicately accomplished one might say almost before it has begun.

Having been conducted to my suite at the Grande I proceeded to stock up with a few luxuries to see me through the next forty-eight hours, having determined to spend the two days resting in comfort at the hotel, rather than wasting time wallowing in the fleshpots of the Holy City.

Accordingly I ordered a dozen bottles of Veuve Cliquot, half a dozen bottles of Claret, I think it was a Margaux, a selection of spirits, and a pound of caviare.

When these had been brought to the room I picked up the telephone and dialled the number on the piece of paper which Driver Lane had instructed Driver Tibbs to pass to me in case I should not be fixed up.

Lucia was both blonde and everything that Driver Lane had said she would be. I suppose very crudely one can divide girls into two categories, the active and the passive, or the giver and the taker. Lucia was in the top league of the former.

I think it would be unnecessary to recount the games we played together during those idyllic forty-eight hours. Possibly they might also sound incredible and I would hate to be accused of sexual boasting. In fact now that I am in my fifties I sometimes find them difficult to believe myself.

Many years later when I saw the film version of Tom Jones, during the highly erotic eating scene at the inn I was vividly reminded of Lucia. I don't think I have ever met a girl with such a voracious appetite for both food and drink and she confirmed my opinion that both have a strong affinity with sex.

Before tea time we had consumed the pound of caviare and were tucking into a second jar, four of the bottles of Veuve Cliquot were empty, and she was demanding steak. This last particularly appealed to me. It may be true that one should beware of the Greeks bearing gifts, although I have never personally met any, but certainly one should be on one's guard against girls ordering steak.

At about seven o'clock Lucia intimated that the time had come for me to take her shopping and, thanking Driver Lane with all my heart for supplying both her and the cash with which to entertain her, we rolled out of bed, dressed and made our way down the Via Veneto.

I have to confess that I was extremely proud to have Lucia hanging on to my arm. Even allowing for the extremely high standard of feminine beauty taking part in the evening promenade, I can honestly say that she led the field by several lengths. To see the envious glances of senior ranking officers as they shamefacedly shuffled by with their trollops afforded me a childlike pleasure. At the same time I was conscious that the honour of the Royal Army Service Corps was being upheld.

While I waited at one of the sidewalk cafes sipping champagne Lucia did her shopping. After an hour she returned wearing a ravishing golden silk trouser suit that caused even more eyes to turn her way and male Italian eyebrows to rise in the severest disapproval. At this point my joy reached a state of ecstasy and as soon as we had finished a second bottle of champagne I seized her by the arm and conducted her back to the Grande, where we fell into one another's arms.

My bills at the Grande, the dress shops and the cafes were just under seven hundred and fifty pounds for forty-eight hours which was approximately double a subaltern's pay for a year.

Sadly I realized that duty must sometimes call and when Driver Tibbs, looking considerably whiter and the worse for wear than when we had parted two days before, arrived at the hotel, I gave my darling Lucia a farewell kiss, cried a little, climbed with difficulty into my fifteen-hundredweight, and ordered Tibbs to cast off and make for the beaches of Salerno.

Taking Route six we drove through a succession of villages and towns utterly devastated by the war. At the time it seemed to me that it would be impossible that these places could ever be rebuilt; indeed it might be better to start from the beginning and create new towns rather than to attempt to reconstitute these heaps of rubble inhabited by a new race of troglodytes. We went through the remains of Valomonte, Ferentino and Frosinone, and I noticed that everywhere on either side of the roads there were still warnings of mines. The approaches to the River Liri were also still heavily mined. On the other side of the river we entered the deserted valley whose small villages and hamlets had simply ceased to exist. Then, bearing to the left, we saw above us the remains of the Monastery of Montecassino.

The Monastery was said to have been one of the key positions in the Italian campaign during the months between the autumn of 1943 and the spring of 1944. Here the Germans held a defensive line known as the Gustav Line which ran from Pesaro to Minturno cutting diagonally across the Apennines. The Allied Commanders searched deep into their hearts before they decided to drop bombs on the monastry. After the bombardment only the tombs of Saint Benedict and Saint Scolastica remained intact, no doubt a miracle in the eyes of all good Roman Catholics. The cloisters were completely destroyed as was the famous basilica.

Ironically, the destruction of the monastery achieved little. The trouble about dropping bombs is that they produce such a shambles that they obstruct the attacking side. Tanks in particular find it impossible to move through rubble.

Leaving the sinister remains of the Monastery behind us we drove through the non-existent town of Cassino itself and out past the large Military Cemetery where lay, side by side, the dead of what was at that time known as the British Empire or Commonwealth of Nations. Even then it was difficult to understand why these men had come from distant parts of the world to die in this alien land; today it is downright impossible.

Just under two hours later we crossed the River Volturno at Capua, and at once it was as if we had re-entered a reactivated zone of war. On all sides large trucks thundered to and fro, splendid American trucks with four-wheel-drive which would have been the envy of every one of my drivers who had had to make do during the war with transport eminently suitable for the Great West Road and designed with no thought of mud, mountains, or other obstacles unlikely to be encountered in peacetime England. On all sides Jeeps tooted and swept by, driven by officers of all ranks from Captains to full Generals, the latter conspicuous by flags fluttering gaily from the bonnets or shields bearing stars.

'To think we had to drive bloody shit and just look at all this beautiful stuff,' Tibbs said bitterly.

I must confess that I could not help thinking that even in my humble capacity I would have been better served with a Jeep as a method of transport than a fifteen-hundredweight which had only to smell mud at twenty miles distance and it would refuse to go further.

Finally, on our left, we saw the heart of all this great activity, the Palace of Caserta, the Headquarters of the Allied Armies in Italy. Begun by one of the Bourbons at the end of the eighteenth century it took some eighty years to complete and has been called the Versailles of Italy. But not even its thousand rooms were enough to house this army of military *élite*. The vast parkland to its north was filled with tents and huts. Everywhere there were other ranks and officers of all nations striding and riding about, each one on a mission of the utmost importance. It was said that, during the course of the Italian Campaign, the equivalent of three divisions were permanently on active service in or around the Palace of Caserta. Not even Churchill, who was forever exhorting his subordinates to get the forces to the sharp end, was able to shift this immoveable force.

I state this as a fact not as a criticism. To tell the truth, I only wish I had played my cards more carefully, been considerably more obsequious, sucked in the right places, and I might have secured myself a place in the Palace for the duration. I knew one subaltern who had passed out with me from O.C.T.U. in late 1941 who spent the entire war in Italy at Allied Headquarters doing nothing except planning his promotion. The system was simple. In peacetime his hobby had been racing pigeons. Having convinced a field-ranking officer in Signals that pigeons were vital to the war effort, he was taken into the staff of Allied Headquarters as a Lieutenant, Royal Army Service Corps (Pigeons), his job being to find suitable birds. The next step was to take on more junior officers. As soon as he had managed to convince his immediate superior that the pigeon business needed more subalterns, he had automatically been promoted to Captain. When these two subalterns needed more help, they had two more subalterns posted on the strength which entitled them to move up to Captains, while my friend moved on to Major. Needless to say everyone above him moved up one rank. It was a kind of snakes and ladders, but provided one wasn't actually sick over the Army Commander's boots it was all ladders and no snakes.

The pigeons were initially cared for by one other rank. There were some hundred or more birds. At the end of hostilities, there was a Regimental Sergeant Major, a Company Sergeant Major, two Staff Sergeants, three Sergeants and six Corporals in whose charge there were twenty-two over-fed and under-exercised birds.

Evening was drawing in as we drove into Salerno and made our way to the beaches that lay to the south of the town. It had been a long day and I was feeling tired. Lascivious thoughts of Lucia began to assail me and I cursed myself for not letting the war in the Far East await my assistance for a further twenty-four hours.

As we went through Salerno I noticed that there were some signs of reconstruction and the streets were filled with people.

We drove south out of the city on the Battipaglia Road until we came to the Montecorvino Airfield and then turned towards the sea.

It must have been about eight o'clock that July evening when Driver Tibbs and I bumped down the final track and were halted by a guard at the barbed wire that surrounded the Royal Army Service Corps D.U.K.W.* Company.

The Corps was proud of its nautical tradition and its members were particularly delighted to think that in a small way it usurped the role of the British Navy, much to the indignation of the stuffy members of the Senior Service. Its Motor Boat Companies were its pride and all ranks would have considered it an honour to be posted to one. A friend of mine from O.C.T.U. spent the entire war drifting round the Mediterranean in a caique. I don't know what he did, and he is vague about it. However, he learned to play the guitar. I suppose after the Tank Transporter Companies, the Water-Borne Companies were the smartest mobs in which to serve. I believe a few officers of the Corps pretended to be cavalrymen and managed to ride about on horses for the duration, but they were few and far between. In Italy the Corps was reduced to handling mules, nasty animals at the best of times. There was certainly nothing glamorous in trying to force them to negotiate goat tracks up the sides of mountains with the temperature several degrees below zero.

I am not sure how the Corps got its D.U.K.W.'s., which obviously should have been manned by the Navy. But get them it did and it clung to them and steadfastly refused to let them go. Roughly the function of the D.U.K.W. was to reinforce the Navy's role by ferrying men and stores from the ships anchored off shore to the beaches and then on inland

*An American built amphibious troop-carrying vehicle.

without transferring the load. I suppose because they were amphibious, they were not considered suitable for men of the Royal Navy.

The guard saluted me. 'The Major's expecting you, Sir. You'll find him on the beach. The Officers' Mess is straight down the line, the big marquee at the end.'

I climbed down from the truck and went into the Officers' Mess.

A Corporal wearing a white mess jacket was polishing the glasses behind a bar in the ante-room.

'Ah, you'll be Mr Nelson, Sir. The Major said to be sure to see you had a drink on arrival to get the dust out of your throat. What'll it be?'

My spirits rose. Was it possible that I was once again after all my vicissitudes to fall on my feet? Was the Major going to turn out to be another Tommy?

'What do they drink here?'

'The Frascati on ice is very popular, Sir.'

'That'll do me. Would it be in order for my driver to have one too?'

'Of course, Sir,' said the Corporal. He took a bottle from a hay box packed with ice and filled two large glasses.

'Who is the Major?' I asked.

'Major Windthrop, Sir. Late of the Brigade.'

'Interesting.'

'Caught one here on the beaches two years ago. Been down-graded and sent to command this shower, if you'll forgive the expression. You'll like him, Sir. A real gentleman.'

Having instructed the Corporal to show Driver Tibbs where to stow my kit, put up my bed and to make me generally comfortable, I wandered on through the camp in the direction of the sea. As I drew near to the shore the noise of shouting and merriment grew louder.

I crossed the final ridge of sand and there before me was the whole of the Company taking its evening swim in the nude. I stopped and admired the scene, and the Far East receded into the distance.

A large man with fair hair came out of the water and started to walk towards me.

'I'm Major Windthrop,' he said holding out a wet hand. 'I don't have to tell you that everyone calls me Windy.'

I noticed a large scar running down his right side.

'Not very pretty, is it?' he said. 'It's amazing how much punishment the body can stand. Unfortunately that particular shrapnel splinter sliced my lung in half.'

I decided that it would be out of order to salute my new Commanding Officer in his birthday suit so I said, 'Glad to meet you, Sir.'

'I've got a friend of yours who is longing to see you again,' he said. 'In fact he's been boring the pants off us telling us what a drunken bastard you are. I'm afraid he doesn't rate your military capacity very high either.' He turned and waved towards the sea.

The next moment John Fish ran out of the water up the beach to join us.

'Well I'll be damned,' I said. 'No one told me you'd be here.'

'I've always been fascinated by Japanese girls,' said John. 'Come on, lets go to the mess. This calls for a drink. Coming, Windy?'

'I'll have a word with the Sergeant-Major first,' said Major Windthrop. 'You two go ahead.' He turned and bellowed: 'Sergeant-Major!'

A short man came out of the water, ran up the beach and came to attention naked in front of Major Windthrop.

'Oh, for goodness sake stand at ease,' said Major Windthrop. 'Please don't let me have to tell you again. When you're stark bollock naked you simply must regard yourself as off parade. Understood?'

'Sir,' bellowed the Sergeant-Major.

Major Windthrop sighed. 'Right, Sergeant-Major, sound the bugle and get the men back to camp. I'll be round to see the food served. I hear it wasn't up to standard last night. Remind me to have a word with the Corporal cook. I've got a feeling he may have something on his mind.'

'All he's got on his mind is that bit of crumpet in Salerno. Fallen for her in a big way, Sir.'

John picked up a towel, slung it round his waist and led me back to the Officers' Mess.

When he had poured me a drink I said: 'It seems all right here, John.'

'You're joking. It's bloody marvellous. Windy's a first rate chap. Knows bugger all about transport, let alone D.U.K.W.'s. In fact I don't think he's ever looked under a bonnet. If he did he'd get a shock at what he saw. He's almost in your class. He leaves all the technical stuff to the N.C.O.'s. Says that's what they're paid for. According to him an officer's job is to look after the morale of the men, and lead them in battle when the time comes.'

'Oh no,' I said. 'Just my luck to get an ex-Guards Officer as a Commanding Officer.'

After we had drunk a bottle of the Frascati John said:' Right, time to dress for dinner. Windy insists on it. I don't suppose you've got any decent togs, but we'll go into Salerno tomorrow and get you kitted out by a tailor I know there.'

I cannot recall much of that first evening in Major Windthrop's Mess, except that I felt very much at home, and all the anxieties that had assailed me on my journey south were soon swamped in a flood of alcohol. Even the Far East seemed far away.

The next morning I reported to Major Windthrop in his tent that served as an office and orderly room and he proceeded to outline my duties. 'You are technically in charge of one of the platoons. But the D.U.K.W.'s are incredibly ancient, and most of them are out of commission. All I want you to do as far as they are concerned is to learn to drive the darned things. Your platoon Sergeant will instruct you. It's just a matter of remembering to engage the gears when you come out of the surf. Apart from that, on John's advice, I am making you entertainments officer. Your duty will be to keep the men amused. There are cricket and darts teams already in operation. There is plenty of swimming and I am arranging with a Motor Boat Company in Naples to loan us a speedboat so that we can get in some water skiing. I also want you to arrange picnics for the men in small parties. Get them out into the moutains. There's Paestum and of course Pompeii, but I expect they'll only be interested in the brothel area there. Very amusing it is too. It will also be your duty to supplement the rations with local produce, excepting vino which is in John's capable hands. 'So, it's up to you. If you can keep the men happy I shall be happy. Working hours are from 0800 to 1300. Then the entire company bathes for an hour and food is served at 1400 hrs after which they are free until the evening bathe at 1900. So you see they've got a lot of free time to fill in and that's where you come in. By the way, there's no need to worry about cash. Regimental Funds are loaded. The Company Sergeant-Major also has a reserve which can be drawn on if necessary.' Major Windthrop paused. 'I don't suppose I have to tell you that the main problem round here is women, or rather the lack of them. You may have noticed some poxy scrubbers hanging around outside the wire. The Regimental Police have strict instructions to pick them up, drive them up into the mountains and dump them. It may seem harsh, but at least its effective. They're all clapped up to the eyes, and in spite of frequent warnings I regret to say that we have already suffered half-a-dozen casualties. Any thoughts about this?'

'Every other army in the world runs its own brothels,' I said. 'It's only the British Army that's forced by a lot of bloody puritans sitting on their arses at home to pretend that soldiers don't feel sexy and when they do they shouldn't'.

'Exactly,' said Major Windthrop enthusiastically. 'That will be another of your duties.'

'What will be?'

'I am asking you, not ordering you, and indeed I have not even

89

suggested it, to set up a camp brothel. I have already discussed it with John. You will be responsible for establishing two brothels one for N.C.O.'s and one for the Drivers.'

'You're joking?'

'I have never been more serious in my life.'

'Haven't you forgotten something, Sir?'

'What?'

'The Officers' knocking shop.'

'What an extremely vulgar expression,' he said. 'My officers will fend for themselves.'

I saluted, left the office and went in search of John, to discover whether Windy had been joking or serious.

'No, he means it all right,' said John. 'He wanted me to take the job on, but I've got rather a lot on my plate at the moment. Besides I didn't think the role suited me. More up your street.'

Knowing John's partiality for the girls I was surprised by this remark.

'Well, how far have you progressed in setting up the brothels?' I asked.

'It only remains to finalize the deal. The question of payment has to be settled. I'll take you into Salerno this afternoon to meet the Madame, but don't expect too much of the girls. They're a bit on the ropey side.'

Later that afternoon I found myself in the salon of one of the Madames who ran the brothels of Salerno discussing terms.

After lengthy haggling it was agreed that there should be one price for all ranks, the equivalent of one pound payable in lire or the wallpaper issued by the Allied Military Government Occupied Territories. The girls would be inspected daily by the Italian doctor who usually only carried out a medical check once a week. The girls would be warned that there was to be no lifting of wallets, watches, rings, cash, indeed of any valuables and any one caught doing so would be instantly dismissed. Furthermore that for the sum of a pound all ranks should be entitled to ten minutes of the girl's time; anything over that was open to mutual bargaining.

To make the proposition really attractive to the local whores, and to ensure that we obtained the best possible service available, it was agreed that each girl working at the camp should be on the strength and entitled to a daily ration similar to that of the men. This of course was our trump card, as food was still in very short supply particularly in the south.

To seal the deal Madame produced a bottle of Strega and three small glasses. I had noticed before that Italians were often very mean with their drinks.

When the toast had been drunk to the success of the enterprise she said, 'And now no doubt the Capitano would care to amuse himself with the girls? Yes?'

'No,' said John.

You could have knocked me down with a feather. 'Are you feeling all right?' I asked.

'Perfectly,' John replied somewhat coldly. 'I am aware that your animal instincts must be assuaged and that you can hardly be expected to rise above them and behave like a human being . . .'

'Are you sure you're all right?'

'There are some of us with more self control, some sense of dignity and spirituality,' continued John, ignoring my question. 'By all means indulge your animal lust. See you back in the camp for dinner.'

I was so shocked that any idea of dalliance with Madame's girls evaporated. Bidding her a hurried farewell I ran out of the brothel and caught John up in the street.

'What's going on?'

John looked down at me, shaking his head sadly. 'There comes a time in our lives, my dear Michael, when we must put aside childish things and try to be our age.' He got into his truck, nodded to Driver Jacks, and drove away, leaving me standing dumbfounded on the pavement.

I was really worried about John. As I made my way back to the camp two odd things struck me. To begin with why had he recommended to Windy that I should set up the brothels? He was more than capable of doing it himself and it was right up his street. What was it that he had said to me the previous day? 'I don't think the job suits me.' It had struck me as peculiar at the time. Now it stood out like a raw sore. And the second point: was I not right in thinking that during the session in the Mess the previous evening John had remained more or less sober? Wasn't I right in recollecting the way he had kept looking at me with a sad and pitying expression? I remembered that at the time it had made me feel uncomfortable. It was as if I had been back at school being reprimanded by one of my schoolmasters and told that I could do better if I tried. The more I thought of John's behaviour, the more mystified I became.

My second evening in the Mess was even more hilarious than the first. We dined exceedingly well. The first course consisted of mullet which had been bombed just beyond the surf in sufficient quantities to feed the entire camp. They were followed by roast suckling pig, a gift from the Sergeants' Mess, about which we asked no questions. To end the meal there were several kinds of cheeses and bowls of peaches, figs, nectarines and apricots.

After this rich meal, it was decided that the only possible drink was brandy. Unfortunately the only one available was a recently brewed Stock, but at least if it was weak on quality, it was strong on quantity.

It must have been about midnight when I found myself racing towards the sea with my fellow officers. For all I know there may have been some Sergeants with us because at one point that evening we enjoyed the hospitality of the Sergeants' Mess. That was the cause of my downfall.

Leaping into the first D.U.K.W. I started the engine and headed it towards the surf, which for the time of year was considerable, as it was blowing half a gale.

I can vaguely remember a very bright moon lighting the scene as I raced towards the water. The waves thundered against the front of the vehicle, lifting it almost vertically and nearly turning it over onto its back. I held it steadily into the waves. I was fairly skilled at this, having many years ago learned to launch dinghies in heavy seas from the Devon beaches. The secret was to keep the boat at right angles to the waves. Any deviation and over she would roll.

Suddenly I found myself beyond the surf and wallowing between the high waves, with my propellor now and again coming right out of the water so that the engine raced and the craft shuddered. All round me were the lights of the other craft that had managed to get seaborn.

Not pausing to think, I stopped the engine and dived overboard. This was extremely foolish. With half a gale blowing my D.U.K.W. immediately started to drift away from me towards the shore which was by now some five or six hundred yards away. I have never been a strong swimmer, and as a result of the food and drink, I was even less capable than usual I turned over and allowed myself to float. It was very strange, lying on my back staring up at the full moon, while all around me the enormous waves swept by, raising me to their pinnacles one minute, then dropping me down into the trough the next. It was like being on a switch-back railway. The water was warm. The sensation was pleasant. But suddenly I knew that I was going to drown. It was an extraordinary sensation. I did not panic. I was not even frightened. Instead I thought to myself: 'So this is it. Into thy hands, O God, I commend my spirit. God bless Mummy, Daddy, John, Joan, Lawrence and Pat.'

These were the names of my sister and brothers.

Then I said aloud: 'To die upon the midnight unseen. To die upon the midnight unseen.'

The water came over my face. I struggled. For the first time I felt desperate, not with fear, but with suffocation. I could remember a mask being placed over my face when I was about seven and the ether being pumped into it prior to my tonsils being removed.

Then blackness. First the struggle, then nothing.

I woke up on the beach. I was lying face downwards in the sand. Someone was leaning on my back, pressing me down, then relaxing, and I knew that I was still alive and someone was applying artificial respiration.

I heard Windy say: 'Thank God for that. He'll be all right. What on earth came over the silly sod? I think we'd better call it a day after this.'

I was ashamed of myself the next morning, ashamed for getting out of my craft and letting it drift away. This is a common cause of drowning. I was aware of the danger involved, and I should have known better. I did not regard brandy as a sufficient excuse.

I had been saved by Major Windthrop who had noticed my D.U.K.W. drifting past with no one in it. He had made an immediate search with the other craft, and luckily come upon me at the very moment that I was disappearing beneath the waves. When I went to his tent to thank him he simply said, 'It was a good party, wasn't it? I shouldn't do that again. How is the brothel business coming along?'

'Should be operating at full strength in a couple of days, Sir.'

The official opening took place forty-eight hours later. I didn't know what the official method of opening a brothel should be, but I arranged for the Company Sergeant-Major to inaugurate the N.C.O's establishment for free, while a bugler sounded *Come to the Cookhouse Door Boys*, better known as *Come and Get It*.

As far as the Drivers were concerned, knowing how much Driver Lane would approve, I allocated a sufficient sum from the currency reserve he had given me, to enable all those drivers who felt so inclined to satisfy what John had come to refer to as 'the nasty side of their natures.'

I was becoming extremely worried about John. Perhaps it would be truer to say that I missed his company. He fulfilled all his regimental duties, appeared at morning parade immaculately turned out by Driver Jacks as usual, attended instruction on how the D.U.K.W.'s could be taken apart and put together, but the life and laughter had gone out of him. No longer was he the rip-roaring lad I had soldiered with in the Middle East, Sicily and up the back of Italy. His consumption of liquor in the mess dropped like a thermometer at the North Pole. Sometimes he sipped a glass of Marsala or white wine before meals, with which he

93

drank water. This was dangerous as the water supply in Salerno was decidedly dodgy. After lunch he would disappear from the camp, and again in the evening after dinner there would be no sign of him.

What annoyed me was that he began to look so healthy. His weight began to fall away and he began to regain the slim figure that had been his when I had first met him in 1942 before we were sent overseas.

Most worrying of all was his complete indifference to the opposite sex. He had expressed his disapproval of the camp brothels. He had not been amused when I regaled him with the sordid details of an adventure I had experienced with a whore in the Off Limits district of Naples and had unkindly remarked: 'If you go on like that, my dear Michael, it can only mean one thing. The pox hospital. In case you think the modern drugs are the answer I would remind you that their long term efficiencies cannot be known for many years to come. It is possible that one day you may want to get married and may find yourself in the position of not having been fully cured. That wouldn't be very nice for your wife, would it?'

I was dumbfounded. My first reaction was to think that John had turned queer. It was unbelievable, but it was the only answer that made sense.

About two weeks after I had arrived at Salerno, Driver Tibbs brought me my morning cup of tea laced with the usual two jiggers of brandy and remarked: 'I've got the answer, guvnor.'

'What answer?'

'The Captain, Sir. Your mate Captain Fish. I've found out his little secret. Driver Jacks was stoned out of his fucking mind in the canteen last night and let the cat out of the bag.'

I sat bolt upright, forgetting the pain of my hangover.

'It's love, Sir. The poor sod's in love.'

'Go on.'

'He's got this bit of Italian stuff up in Nocera. According to Jacks she's a bit of all right. Only sixteen and never been—if you get my meaning. Captain Fish has fallen hook, line and sinker for her. Driver Jacks reckons his intentions are honourable.'

'Never,' I said.

'He wants to do the right thing by her, church her and all that malarky.'

My hangover receded into the background. I put my feet firmly onto the coconut matting which covered the sand and said: 'Driver Tibbs, you're a man after my own heart. Have you any problems? The Company Sergeant-Major is not trying to put you on the guard roster is he? Everything's all right with you?'

'Perfectly, guv'nor.'

'Then there's nothing I can do for you? I know. Take a couple of days off. I will fend for myself for forty-eight hours.'

'Like fucking hell you can,' said Driver Tibbs.

I thought to myself how lucky I had been with my batmen, without whom I would never have survived. First Driver Lane, an idle soldier but a brilliant financier, and now Driver Tibbs, totally loyal and dedicated to my well-being.

We had just come off maintenance instruction on the amphibious vehicles and I was walking towards the Mess with John when I remarked casually: 'I'm so glad to hear of your romance, John. I was very worried about you. I thought you would never settle down.'

'You shit.'

'When am I going to meet her?' I asked.

'Never. She's the kind of girl I only propose to introduce to gentlemen and respectable members of society.'

I was annoyed at this slur on my character. 'Does Major Windthrop know about this?'

As John did not reply I assumed that Major Windthrop was not included in the aforementioned categories.

'Then let me remind you, John,' I continued. 'Romances which may lead to marriage are severely frowned upon by higher authority. Did you not read the Army Order which suggested that officers and other ranks in love with local girls should be posted away for a period of not less than six months? Now I should hate to lose you and I'm sure Windy would too, but Army Orders are made to be obeyed.'

'You're a shit, Michael,' said John. 'You're a blackmailing, fucking shit.'

'I have my duty to carry out.'

'Duty!' shouted John, and I feared he might burst a blood vessel. 'Duty! Since when have you ever thought of duty, you cowardly, scrounging, useless, drunken bum?'

'That kind of abuse will get you nowhere,' I said. 'My duty compels me this very minute to inform Windy.'

'You win,' said John. 'Though I'll get it back on you one day, you little sod. I'll take you to meet Maria this evening.'

'Maria. What a common name,' I said.

'No nonsense though. You're to behave yourself. No getting drunk, no swearing, and if you so much as try to lay a finger on her I'll personally break your bloody back.'

The rest of the day dragged by, so keen was I to view this girl who had had such a disastrous effect on John's character.

We drove out to Nocera in John's personal jeep. As a water-borne company of the R.A.S.C. we were extremely short of transport. Instead of fifteen-hundredweights and a staff car for the Commanding Officer, all the officers were entitled to a baby D.U.K.W. As these were either non-existent or non-starters, transport presented a real difficulty. John had solved his problem by buying a Jeep from the Americans in Naples. He had been forced to trade in a whole case of unadulterated Scotch for it, which I thought an excessive price to pay. At least he should have diluted this valuable commodity with fifty per cent distilled water, easily procurable from the workshops section.

Nocera lay about half-way between Salerno and Pompeii and had been the scene of bitter fighting some two years before, so that little of it had been left standing.

We turned off what remained of the main street and made our way between piles of rubble and ruined houses to the outskirts of the town, where John stopped the Jeep in front of what I can only describe as a peasant's hovel, or rather what was left of one.

The walls were propped up with roughly hewn supports. Gaping gaps in the roof were covered over with the remains of beaten-out petrol cans, and the windows with hessian camouflage nets. From the chimney, constructed of empty twelve pound margarine tins, although it was summer, came a wisp of smoke. It was a very lowly dwelling indeed.

John took a bulging sack from the back of the Jeep, went to the door which was the grandest piece of the establishment, and had clearly come from some much bigger house, and gently tapped with the knocker.

The door was opened by an aged crow dressed in black from head to foot, who muttered some inaudible words of greeting, displaying as she did so a solitary and extremely dirty fang. I can't say I admired John's future mother-in-law. She cast a rapacious look at the sack which John was carrying, and even before he had given it to her, had started to feel its contents, mumbling strange imprecations in a Neapolitan dialect as she did so.

I followed them into the house.

Through the gloom and the smoke coming from a large open fire-place I could make out the figure of a girl on her knees fanning a handful of twigs. At the table sat a large man in his braces. His face was red and boasted a large black moustache that drooped at both ends in the wad that was to become fashionable on the King's Road in London some thirty years later.

'Mama,' said John 'this is the Tenente Michele of whom I have told you so much. Papa, the Tenente Michele.'

I shook hands.

John then took me towards the girl who was fanning the flames in the hearth. From the top of the fireplace there was suspended a black cast iron pot, whose contents gave out the smell of concentrated garlic.

'Maria, my love, this is my friend, Michele.'

The girl looked up at me without smiling, and returned to the serious business of cooking.

Behind me I heard a door close as Mama disappeared carrying the sack of food that John had brought with him, no doubt to conceal it in some cache.

Although Maria had shown no wish to get to know me further, I had to confess that she was a real beauty in the conventional Italian style. Her hair was jet black, her face very pale with a tinge of brown. Her fingers were long and beautifully tapered, although I would have preferred it had she removed the dirt from under her nails. Like her mother she was dressed in black, a black skirt and a black cotton blouse. The latter did nothing to conceal the charming protusion of her breasts.

'A lovely bit of crumpet,' I commented.

John frowned and seated himself on a small stool that stood inside the fireplace.

I walked back into the room and sat down opposite Papa, from where I could only dimly make out John as the smoke from the twigs curled around him. I do not know how long I sat there. From the fireplace I could hear John muttering away in Pidgin Italian. Occasionally the girl replied, but so softly that I could not distinguish a single word she was saying.

It must have been after about half an hour that Mama reappeared and whispered something in Papa's ear who immediately called out in Italian which I was able to understand: 'Mama says you have brought no tinned milk. Would you kindly not forget next time as the child will die if she does not have milk.'

What child Mama was referring to I did not know. Perhaps she meant her Maria who certainly looked as if she needed fattening up.

From the fireplace came the sound of spluttering as John coughed his heart up in the smoke. By now my eyes, although streaming, had become accustomed to the gloom, and I noticed a bunch of fish hanging by their heads over the fire to be smoked. It occurred to me that if John didn't look out he would be very nicely kippered too.

After an hour of sitting in silence, broken only by John's whisperings from the fireplace, the occasional cackle of a chicken, and what sounded like the moo of a cow from the room next door, I became bored. If this was love, John was welcome to it. I was about to suggest that I go and find a bar in Nocera where John could pick me up when his courting was finished for the day, when I noticed that Papa had turned his chair so that he could keep an eye on the lovers.

John had carefully moved his stool so that he was now next to Maria, and I noticed that he had begun to stroke her hair with his right hand. The only effect this seemed to have on her was to make her crouch even lower over the fire.

The next thing I knew was that Papa had gone to the cupboard and returned to the table bringing with him an ancient fowling piece. It really was incredibly old, and I noticed that there were holes half way down the barrel, and the stock was held together with binding twine. I very much doubted whether it could be fired. Of one thing I was certain. If Papa intended to loose it off in John's direction to defend his daughter's virginity, I for one had no wish to be anywhere near it. But thinking it only fair to warn John of his and my danger I said: 'John, the old man's got a gun. I don't think your right hand should stray any further.'

'I really don't think you should be so crude, Michael.' said John.

I was affronted. 'John,' I said, 'we have soldiered together from Alamein to the Alps. I merely thought it would be a tragedy should the Reaper come for you now. To be honest I have a feeling that your presence is not welcome in this highly desirable residence. There is a something in the atmosphere which I can only describe as '*antipatico*'. However honourable your intentions may be, clearly they are highly suspect in the eyes of both Mama and this brigand.'

'I think you had better go,' said John. 'It was a mistake to have brought you here. It was stupid of me to think that you could recognize love when you saw it.'

'I shall wait for you at the first bar in what is left of the High Street.'

I rose, bade farewell to Mama, Papa and Maria, not one of whom answered me a word, and walked out into the fresh air of the Italian summer.

When John finally picked me up at midnight, he drove me back to camp, without speaking a word to me. I thought it wisest not to attempt to draw him into a conversation. Love does the strangest things to the best of us.

Driver Tibbs brought me my nightcap as I lay on my camp bed pondering over the mysteries of love and sex.

'Message for you from Major Windthrop,' he said handing me an envelope marked CLASSIFIED.

I ripped it open and read as follows:

To Lt. Nelson, Entertainments (B.).

Congratulations on the good work. Understand girls much appreciated and all clean so far. Lunch with me tomorrow Zia, Naples, Windy.'

The next day, after the third dozen risky oysters from the bay of Naples and the fourth bottle of a dry Frascati, I asked Windy what B in brackets stood for. 'Brothels, you nit,' he replied.

Chapter Six

One morning, some three weeks after I had arrived on the beaches of Salerno, I was listening to the Company Sergeant-Major lecturing on the machinery of D.U.K.W.'s when I received an order to report to Major Windthrop.

Casting my mind back across the events of the previous evening, wondering if I had been sick over the Major's boots, whom I had insulted, or what other crime I might have committed under the influence of too much drink, I hurried to his tent.

'I have good news for you, Michael,' said Major Windthrop as soon as I had saluted and seated myself in a chair facing him. 'You go on leave tomorrow.'

'I don't particularly want to go, Sir. I'm happy here in this holiday camp. I had enough of the Roman fleshpots on my way down to keep my horrible nature satisfied for a few more weeks. To tell you the truth I think this Italian brandy will finish it off once and for all. You know, Windy, I've read a great deal about the effects of alcohol on one's sexual . . .'

'Some other time, Michael,' said Windy, rudely interrupting what I thought might be a fruitful basis for discussion. 'You are going on leave to England.'

'You're joking,' I said. I had long since put out of my mind all thought of leave home. I had put in for it. I was entitled to it. Ironically the military authorities in their perversity kept sending home their more efficient officers while insisting on retaining the services of useless ones like myself.

'You leave tomorrow. Report midday to the transit camp. I assume you will dine in mess tonight so that we can celebrate the event in a suitable manner?'

'Oh, not again,' I said.

'Nelson, I trust you are not weakening. May I suggest that you take a bath before dinner to get yourself into a suitable state of mind. By the way, I have told your friend John to be present. He didn't take too kindly to the suggestion.' He leant forward and became confidential. 'Tell me, Michael, what's the matter with John? Recently he hasn't been the man I used to know.'

'My lips are sealed, Windy,' I said, 'Rather, it's more than my life is worth at John's hands if I tell you. So please don't press me. If I say that love is the trouble, I must leave the rest to you.'

'Thought as much. Who would have thought John Fish would have got it so badly? Ah well, let's hope it doesn't last. The worst thing in the world is a reformed rake.'

There was nothing special about the party that night. We drank a great deal, launched the D.U.K.W.'s, sank a couple which were retrieved by a special squad that was standing by for such an eventuality. I woke next morning at eleven having been excused all parades and duties by Windy, feeling even more ill than usual. I was forced to ask Driver Tibbs to lace my first cup of tea with double the normal amount of brandy.

As I had said good-bye to everyone the previous evening, without more ado, with Driver Tibbs at the wheel of a D.U.K.W., we proceeded at a cracking pace towards the transit camp at Naples.

When the transit camp came into view I ordered Driver Tibbs to halt, and change places with me, which he did with a surly expression on his face, so that I had to remind him that dumb insolence was an offence under military law.

'Fuck that,' he said. 'The bloody war is over and I have no wish to end up dead or maimed. You know perfectly well you're in no condition to drive. At the best of times you don't know how these bloody things work.'

'Nonsense, Driver Tibbs,' I said letting in the clutch and proceeding at high speed towards the entrance to the camp.

I must confess that my reason for taking over the wheel was not altogether honourable. I wanted to show off. I knew that the men who drove the D.U.K.W.'s in the R.A.S.C. were held in high esteem by the rest of the army. They had done stirring work in hostile conditions, from the original landings at Salerno to the crossings of the River Po. I wanted to share in some of this glory to which I had no claim.

To begin with all went well. I negotiated the main entrance where a couple of Military Policemen threw me up salutes worthy of the parade ground at Caterham.

A D.U.K.W. is somewhat broad in the beam, considerably wider than the average three-ton lorry. As I sped down the central road of the camp I scraped a Jeep coming in the opposite direction, and sent the pedestrians scattering for safety in all directions. Disregarding their shouts of abuse I airily took my hand off the wheel and waved to them courteously.

This proved my undoing. The steering of a D.U.K.W. on land is extremely heavy. Like a waterfowl it is awkward when earth-borne and much prefers the sea. Its wheels hit a pothole which had been carelessly left unfilled by the camp engineers. The steering wheel spun fiercely in my right hand, my left being engaged in waving to the walkers who had narrowly escaped death. The beastly machine took a swerve to the right.

Before I could regain control, the D.U.K.W. had run off the roadway and was careering along the grass verge, gathering speed. I failed to keep my cool, and instead of braking and bringing it to a halt, for some reason I increased the pressure of my foot on the accelerator. All might yet have been well. Unfortunately the guy ropes of a marquee impeded our progress. My vehicle disregarded them and swept forward taking them with it.

From the corner of my eye I had the horrible experience of seeing the marquee begin to collapse, while from under its canvas came shouts of protest and alarm.

Driver Tibbs had the presence of mind to lean across and switch off the ignition. The D.U.K.W. ground to a halt just in time to prevent it from assaulting an even larger tent.

As I climbed down from the D.U.K.W. I was surrounded by an infuriated bunch of officers of Field Rank, that's to say Majors and above, each one of whom had his pet words of abuse to hurl at me.

It had been my ill-fortune to destroy the Senior Officers' Mess. I was thinking my leave might be postponed. Subsequently I came to regard it as one of the more distinguished achievements of my military career.

I was saved from a Court Martial by the intervention of a Major of one of the tank squadrons I had serviced in the last days of the war. Soon after the crossing of the River Po I had taken some shells to his tanks, and had left him a bottle of whisky before retiring from the battle zone. This act of consideration now stood me in good stead.

Within half an hour the damage had been repaired, and I found myself drinking large whiskys in the Senior Officers' Mess. After discreet enquiries I was informed that I had been elected an honorary member of the Mess and was therefore entitled to buy drinks. This I proceeded to do throughout the day, not forgetting to thank Driver Lane once again for supplying me with the necessary capital to indulge myself in this way.

The following day we embarked in a train at Naples and began the long trek towards Calais and so on to England.

The journey was slow and uncomfortable. We were held up for several hours at the Swiss frontier while Swiss soldiers had the impertinence to search the train for I don't know what and to behave in an officious manner.

It is a mistake to imagine Switzerland to be nothing more than the home of the peaceful if irritating cuckoo clock. The Swiss made a very good thing out of their neutrality in the Second World War—as they had done in the First. They sold arms and precision instruments like bomb sights to both sides. Being a nation of small-minded tradesmen all they cared about was the cash. Democrats or Fascists were the same to them. Not for one minute did they allow the smell of burning flesh in the German concentration camps to deter them from their money-grubbing habits.

It has always been a matter of considerable regret to me that the first atomic bomb was not dropped on Switzerland. This would have assured Europe of a happier future, unencumbered by the horrible gnomes of Zurich, who ever since the war have been causing untold misery throughout the world, as they grow fatter and fatter like their bank balances. Besides, I have an antipathy towards mountains. If you climb one there's another which looks exactly the same awaiting you. Switzerland would be a better place for being flattened and denuded of the Swiss.

Finally, somewhat the worse for wear and drink, since Driver Tibbs had thoughtfully stowed a crate of assorted spirits under my seat, which were greatly appreciated by my fellow voyagers and secured for me a universal popularity, we disembarked late one night at Calais. Here we were shepherded into one of the filthiest and most sordid Transit Camps through whose portals it has ever been my misfortune to pass. The supper was inedible and was thrown away and eaten by the rats that swarmed all over the place. The bunks were damp, the blankets filthy, and the whole place smelt of rotting cabbage.

Three days after reaching England I was assailed by acute irritation in my lower regions. Close inspection revealed considerable infestation by a host of crabs. I picked one off and was not surprised at the pain they were causing as I watched it with fascination wave its tiny feet and claws at me. I know one does not catch V.D. off lavatory seats, the old excuse of every greenhorn. Crabs are a different matter. Not having been in close association with any girl for several weeks, I am pretty sure those were Froggie crabs, almost certainly picked up in that disgusting Transit Camp.

I took myself to the chemist at the lower end of Piccadilly, famous for its pick-me-ups after a night on the booze, and I bought myself a tin of blue ointment.

The younger generation does not know how lucky it is. It does not appreciate what science has done for it. Today those little monsters present no problem. One application of some wonder medication, and they die within a few hours. My generation was forced to treat them with Blue Ointment and some people were convinced that the brutes actually liked the stuff. It was a messy treatment. First one had to shave off all one's pubic hair, then spread the ointment over the infected area. Needless to say it stained every piece of clothing with which it came into contact. There was nothing then known to remove the stain.

If one was lucky the pests eventually died. Sometime they beat a retreat to new positions. I met one unfortunate man who, having treated his lower reaches, found that the devils had moved into his hair, and finally made their last stand in his eyebrows. I know this to be true because I was lunching with him one day and saw one of them fall from his right eyebrow into his soup.

My month's leave in England was disappointing. The trouble was that I had expected to return to the same country and the same society that I had left three years before. I had not appreciated to what extent the war had altered the life I had been lucky enough to live before 1939. The First World War had almost finished off the Middle Class, to which I belonged; the Second World War completed the process.

Somehow I had not expected to find my own family so irrevocably scattered. I had been foolish enough to suppose that not even a war would be able to destroy its unity. I had expected to come back to the comforts and sense of security that had surrounded me in our large Ascot house in the days of peace. I was greatly mistaken.

To begin with my mother and father were no longer living together. My father was in the process of securing a second wife. My mother was in a nursing home suffering from melancholia. The house at Ascot was inhabited by vast numbers of evacuees who had reduced it to a pigsty My family were never to return to it. My eldest brother, who had been discharged from the forces as medically unfit, had taken to growing tomatoes. He continued to cultivate the land for several years, but in spite of an acute shortage of food, he never succeeded in making money, which has always been a source of considerable mystery to me. My second brother, Lawrence, was in a rehabilitation centre for pilots, having crashed his plane or fallen out of it; I am not quite sure which; nor, do I think, is he. All I know is that he nearly died. My sister was nursing, and my youngest brother was still at school.

The only person who made any attempt to keep the family together was my grandmother, who had taken a flat in Shepherd Market, off Piccadilly.

She was constantly amazed at the number of beautiful girls who paraded round the Market, and always delighted in pointing out the more striking ones. She considered them really nice girls.

The doorman on her block of flats, although long past the age of desire, would watch them by the hour. He was very willing to pass on to me information as to their performance, cost and other details.

I found that my leave in London was no different from the leaves that I had spent there before I had been sent overseas. There were the same hordes of drunken soldiery of all nations. I went to the same pubs and clubs and although a great number of familiar faces were missing, the atmosphere had not altered, nor the desperate desire on the part of everyone to get as drunk as possible. This was slightly more difficult than it had been three years ago, as there was a shortage of all drinkable spirits, and whisky was in desperately short supply. So much for the Old Country having won the war. It was now fast on its way to losing the peace, a process which has not ceased to this day.

Life, too, was far more expensive than it had been when I had gone away.

Soon after arriving in London I paid a visit to the Ritz to lunch in the restaurant. The main course was a casserole of plovers. Not bad at all. The wine list was abysmal, and I ended up with a Magnum of Champagne for which I was charged eighteen pounds. I could not make use of Driver Lane's fighting reserve which was all in lire, but as I had a considerable amount of money in the bank, not having drawn my army pay for three years, this presented no problem. Nevertheless I asked the management to wrap up the empty Magnum as a souvenir, which they did without a word of protest. Later in the day, finding it somewhat cumbersome, I dropped it in a gutter.

The Café Royal had long been closed for late-night sessions. I discovered that a great number of its clientele had moved to the Gargoyle Club off Dean Street, not to be confused with the present-day Gargoyle Club where ladies remove their clothing.

The Gargoyle Club of those days was a members' club which belonged to David Tennent, one-time husband of Hermione Baddeley. It was frequented by writers, journalists, actors, painters, and riff-raff which included a high percentage of hangers-on and mumpers, the latter being an eighteenth century word for ale-house beggers.

It was reached by a creaking lift that moved upwards at a snail's pace and induced in me such terror that on emerging from it I always made straight for the bar and downed a couple of large whiskys of which there seemed to be an adequate supply at the club. This may have been clever psychology on the part of the proprietor.

The bar was on the same level as the exit from the lift, and downstairs there was a restaurant and dance floor where one could hop about to the music of a three-piece band, which I think was called Alexander's Ragtime Band.

It seemed to me after a few visits to the Gargoyle that a number of its *habitués* had passed a very happy war in its cosy bosom. There were some writers and journalists who had managed to secure themselves pleasant nooks in the Ministry of Information or psychological departments of one of the three services where they were able to indulge in their theories which had not the slightest effect on the outcome of the war. I would be lying if I did not confess that I was made extremely jealous by these lucky people. I was angry with myself for not having played my cards more carefully. It was clear to me that the Establishment had taken good care to look after its own. The old school tie was a useful possession in the last war. It occurred to me although I had been to Bryanston the sensible thing to have done would have been to invest in an old Etonian tie and declared her to have been my alma mater.

If anyone should doubt the strength of the Establishment in those days I would recommend them to read the diaries of Harold Nicolson and the heavily censored ones of that old quean Chips Channon. The upper and middle classes of this country during the twenty years following the Kaiser's war were so convinced of their natural superiority, that I am amazed that the workers didn't arise from their slumbers and wipe them off the face of the earth. The fact that they didn't convinces me that we are not a nation of revolutionaries. The artistic and literary coteries of that era were particularly unpleasant, and among the nastiest was the so-called Bloomsbury Group. Their sense of apartness from the common herd is beyond belief.

The Gargoyle had its fair share of eccentrics and boozers. Robert Newton, the actor, could be observed emerging from the lift supporting himself on two sticks, so drunk that it was an even money bet whether he would make the bar. Sometimes he was speechless; at other times he became violent, and proceeded to bombard anyone to whom he had taken a dislike with gulls eggs. These, unlike those of the hen, were not rationed.

Downstairs Brian Howard could be observed in a no less intoxicated state looking anxiously around the room for someone to insult. If there were no friends available, he was forced to pick on a stranger, and he would not be happy until he had been severely mauled in a fight, and been ejected by a posse of waiters.

One evening I was sitting in the bar by myself when a beautiful girl sat down next to me and commanded me to buy her a whisky. I obliged, not with any ulterior motive. I was far too far gone for thoughts, let alone acts, of love.

Having downed the Scotch at a speed which could not have been good for her complexion she ordered a second, which followed the first as quickly.

I had no objection to paying. I was fascinated by the performance. By the tenth large Scotch I was overcome with admiration, although worried for the condition of her heart.

Trying to be helpful I said: 'Are you all right? Is there anything I can do for you?'

My words had a most amazing effect. Pulling aside her mink coat, which was all she was wearing, she exposed two extremely presentable breasts and screamed at me: 'You're just another of those fucking homosexuals. You don't like my breasts do you? They make you want to vomit, don't they? I suppose you want me to cut the fucking things off?'

To add injury to this insult, she picked up her glass and threw it at my face.

As I could see no further mileage in her, I got off my stool and hurried from the bar, while she continued to shout continuous abuse after me.

During this leave I spent a considerable amount of time drinking in Shepherds, a pub much in favour at the time with the forces, and particularly with the R.A.F. Within its doors one was secure from the importunings of the hundreds of tarts who worked the Market area. Should one come into the bar the landlord at the time would approach the girl in question, hand her a shilling and ask her to leave. This might seem unkind, but as someone drinking at the bar with me remarked: 'I like a bit with the best of them, but I don't actually want it in my beer.'

It was during this leave too that I came to be a member of the Embassy Club in Old Bond Street. Its fashionable days were over. In the thirties it had been the resort of the smart set that included the Prince of Wales. It was smart no longer, but its prices were reasonable. The licensing laws in those days were very different. One had to place an order with the wine merchant for a dozen bottles of everything. One did not pay for them until one wanted one, when a messenger was dispatched to a central wine store and returned bringing with him one of your bottles. In this way the law which said no one should drink after eleven o'clock was successfully evaded, and a very stupid law it was too. I never cease to grow hot under the collar when I think of the licensing laws in operation today. It is monstrous that we should still be suffering for the drunkenness of the munition workers in the Kaiser's war, who were grossly overpaid while their less fortunate brothers were being blown to pieces on the Western Front. To curb their over-indulgence which was adversly affecting the supply of munitions to the unfortunates at the sharp end, Lloyd George brought in the Licensing Hours with powers granted to him under the Defence of the Realm Act. Incredible as it may seem, they still dictate our drinking hours to this day.

Most nights I ended up at the Embassy Club with a party who were only too happy to help me down several bottles of Scotch at a mere two pounds a bottle. I spent liberally and scattered tips right and left thus ensuring that there were always able and helping hands to carry me to a waiting car at the door when oblivion finally descended. Luigi, the head waiter, whose word was final, was extremely kind to me, and whenever possible ensured that I had a ringside seat for the cabaret, imagining that I enjoyed looking at the girls. Little did he know that by the time they appeared, my sight had failed me.

About ten days after my return to England I began to feel exhausted by my constant standing at the bars of public houses and clubs, so I decided to go to the country and visit my brother Lawrence to see how he was recovering from his recent 'prang'. He was waiting for me on the platform as my train drew in and his first comment was: 'Christ, you look bloody rough. You could do with a beer.' I regarded this as a particularly brotherly greeting since we had not met since the last summer of peace. He had departed early in the war to train as a pilot in South Africa, and somehow when he returned to England and I had been inducted into the forces our leaves had never coincided.

In the pub I realized that Lawrence was in pretty poor shape himself. One of his legs was encased in plaster, and there were the remains of several nasty wounds on his face and forehead.

When we left the pub an hour later, Lawrence led me to a magnificent vintage Lagonda, whose bonnet was held down by a strap, a sight which can cause a hearty man to have an orgasm.

When I asked him whether he would like me to drive he angrily waved me aside, threw his crutch into the back, edged himself behind the wheel, and we were away at a terrifying pace in the direction of the R.A.F. rehabilitation centre. Undoubtedly this was one of the most perilous rides I have ever experienced, and as usual I offered up a prayer to God who heard it, and we arrived in one piece at the Centre.

Not quite, in the course of the journey Lawrence's crutch had blown out of the back seat, and I was sent into the Centre to find another.

I spent the rest of the day and the following night at this place, which was an unnerving experience. It was as if I had entered the horrific world of Bosch. On all sides I was surrounded by men suffering from hideous mutilations and burns. Although on the surface the atmosphere was one of hope and courage, I could sense underneath a feeling of despair. But each one of them showed remarkable bravery and it was only their desperate drinking that indicated the underlying pain and fear for what the future might hold for them.

I was the only pongo in the place and although they were not impressed at my being an officer in Ally Slopers Cavalry, they could not accuse me of having spent an idle war in the Old Country. For the first and last time the African and Italian Stars stood me in good stead. I distinguished myself by singing, though that is hardly the right word, fifteen filthy verses of *The Ball of Kirriemuir*. Most people know the tune and the chorus, a few people know two or three verses, but to know fifteen is a considerable achievement. I followed this with a rendering of *There Once was a Gay Caballero*, gay in those days not having the connotation that it has today, and concluded with an extra-obscene rendering of *Eskimo Nell*, after which I was carried to my couch. At least the next morning I had the satisfaction that I had not let Lawrence down.

We were joined the next day by our father who brought with him his future wife. Seeing that our mother was still alive and ill in a Nursing Home this showed considerable courage on his part, even if it was hardly in the best of taste. But I had determined, when he had written to me some months previously in Italy about the situation, not to take a moral stand on the unhappy business. The world is full of people who fall in love and then fall out of it. I was desperately sorry for my mother whom I suspect had never ceased to love my father. But as I had written to him, when one of the partners to a marriage no longer loves the other, nothing in the world can cement that union together again. Under the circumstances it is best to make a break, even if one of them is heartbroken.

I am far more ashamed of my own treatment of my mother. During this leave I went to visit her in the Nursing Home only three or four times, although I know that she desperately wanted to see me. I took her out to lunch, and all the time I was aware of her unhappiness. She was like a child who did not know what she had done wrong. I do not think she knew that my father had fallen in love with someone else, and she could not understand why he had left her. It was pathetic, but there was nothing I could say which would reassure her and restore her confidence. Instead of spending as much time with her as possible I preferred to go drinking and whoring.

My mother died later that year and to this day I bitterly regret having been so selfish. I loved her dearly. My guilt to this day is so strong that I still cannot visualize her or hear her voice.

I was priming the pump in Shepherd Market the following day when I received a slap on the back and, turning round, was greeted by John Fish. I knew that there was a possibility of his coming on leave shortly after me and had told him he would most probably find me at Shepherds every morning at opening time if I was in London.

From Shepherd Market John and I proceeded to my favourite restaurant, Wheeler's in Old Compton Street. After lunch I signed the bill. That was the first time I got into debt at Wheeler's and I have been in it ever since.

The afternoon was disastrous, but I suppose no more than usual because it was no different from the kind of thing that happened on all my leaves in London.

We were in a club off Piccadilly drinking large whiskys at a prohibitive price when John's eye was taken by a striking looking girl with ginger hair who was known to everyone in the bar as Red. I could not help thinking of his Madonna-like Maria back in Italy, but with John, like so many other men, it was out of sight out of mind. I even had the temerity to mention Maria's name.

'That's all over,' he said angrily.

'Bit quick, wasn't it?' I remarked. 'Still, I'm glad you won't have to sit in the fire any more slowly being smoked to death.'

'Very funny. I could have killed that sod of a father. Do you know he had arranged for her to marry some bloody Eytie, and she had no say in the matter? All he wanted off me was bully beef, tinned milk and cigarettes.'

'How did you find this out?'

'She told me. Don't get me wrong. She was a sweet girl. I loved her dearly. But it was hopeless. Those bloody Eyties are still living in Medieval times.'

I was delighted to find for the first time that John was not always successful in love. I thought failure in that quarter was my monopoly.

An hour later we left the club with Red and a couple of bottles of Scotch for which we paid ten pounds each. It seemed a cheap price to pay for the delights that Red had promised us both with her friend.

Her friend was resting at their flat, which was close to Shepherd

Market. When I heard the word friend I reached for my revolver. I had a nasty suspicion that this friend would turn out to be something out of a Breughel painting. John would end up indulging in those mouth-watering games that Red had suggested, while I would have to content myself with talking to the unspeakable friend.

I was also anxious about our condition. I knew that even if the friend was Venus herself, it was doubtful whether she would be able to stimulate my base nature.

As a matter of fact the friend Barbara, or Barb for short, turned out to be a very presentable girl. She came from Yorkshire and I was very attracted by her voice. Although we had woken her from a deep sleep she was extremely good-tempered about it. She threw a flimsy dressing gown round her shoulders which did little to conceal her small but firm breasts, and joined us in tackling the two bottles of Scotch.

I was quietly minding my business with Barb on the sofa who was behaving admirably and suggesting that I take a nap as I was clearly incapable of anything else, when suddenly an almighty row started to brew between John and Red.

The next moment I heard a shout of pain and, looking round, I saw that Red had drawn her nails across John's face, inflicting considerable damage.

The next moment she was standing half naked in the middle of the room screaming: 'Out! Out! Out you go, you filthy bastards!'

I looked at Barb who said: 'You'd better go. She's the boss round here and the very devil when she gets going with her nail file.'

I did not need telling twice.

'Call yourself an officer and a fucking gentleman,' screamed Red. 'You're nothing but a disgusting bloody pervert.'

I scrambled into my battledress blouse, picked up my cap, and made for the door with all possible speed. If there's one thing that terrifies me it's a girl in a temper who has never been introduced to Lord Queensberry.

I did not wait for John, who had managed to retrieve his clothes, and was retreating towards the door trying to put them on and fight a rearguard action at the same time.

'You might bloody well come to my aid,' he called to me.

'Every man for himself,' I shouted.

Catching sight of the remaining full bottle of Scotch, John tried to counter-attack, but was confronted with an even angrier Red, who had now, as Barb had warned me, produced an evil-looking nail-file from her bag.

To my horror this did not deter John. I closed my eyes as he continued his counter-attack, not wishing to see his face slashed to ribbons.

There was a blood-curdling shriek as he closed with her, knocking the weapon from her hand with a perfectly timed piece of unarmed combat.

Red fell to the floor. As John leant over her to seize the whisky she dug her teeth into his leg.

John screamed with pain. Still she held him fast with her teeth.

He started to hop towards the door, dragging her after him. They must have been splendid teeth. I wondered if at some time or other she could have been one of those circus artistes who amuse themselves by hanging by their teeth from a high wire. Not until he had dragged her to the door did she loosen her hold with her fangs. All the time John kept hollering. Clutching his whisky, he ran past me, and bolted down the stairs. I would have liked to have stayed with Barb. At least I would have liked to have got her telephone number, but seeing that Red was about to attack me in turn, and having no wish to be trapped between her jaws, I turned and ran down the stairs after John.

We were followed by a stream of abuse, such as it has been my good fortune never to hear again. I honestly believe that it would have shocked my drivers.

There was no stopping John. Running like a sprinter in the Olympics, he was through the hall and out of the front door as I reached the bottom of the stairs.

I was crossing the hall when the contents of a chamber pot came crashing down on my head. It was a perfect bull's-eye.

From upstairs the screams of abuse gave way to maniacal laughter.

I tottered out into the street, the urine dripping down the back of my neck and over my uniform.

As soon as he saw me John stopped crying and burst into laughter.

I was not amused.

'I think you had better go straight to a doctor and be injected,' I said. 'Those bites could quite likely be syphilitic. While you're about it you'd better consider the danger of rabies. Don't forget the tetanus jabs either.'

'Do you really think so?'

'I've never been more serious in my life,' I said. I was still trying to clean my self up with a handkerchief, and feeling ill.

A minute later I was sick on the steps of the tarts' house much to the disgust of the passers-by.

'An officer too!' I heard one lady, who clearly shopped at Harrods, remark.

When I had recovered my breath I said: 'John, what did you say to her that brought on that exhibition?'

'Never you mind,' said John.

To this day I have not discovered what he said. My mind boggles at what unmentionable practice he must have suggested. I thought I knew them all.

I remember a line of poetry that I read at school: 'A thing to dream of not to tell'. My English master remarked at the time that it was one of the most erotic lines in the whole of English poetry. He was right. I still lie awake in the early hours of the morning, thinking up fantastic acts of love. Not one of them ever seems sufficiently way out to bring on the tantrums that beautiful Red displayed that afternoon in the summer of 1944.

Chapter Seven

I was in mid-channel when the first atomic bomb was dropped on Japan. By the time I had found my way back to the beaches of Salerno to join the D.U.K.W. Company the second bomb had been dropped, and the war was over.

It was difficult at the time to understand exactly what had occurred. Information was scarce. All we knew was that something had happened which had made all the weapons of destruction with which we had become acquainted during the last five years obsolete overnight. It was as if up to that August of 1945 we had been waging war with wooden clubs.

At Salerno I found a very subdued Officers' Mess. Windy was particularly thoughtful. I think he was considering resigning his Regular Commission. He felt out of date from the moment the first atomic bomb was dropped.

Strangely enough the real significance of the situation as far as we were concerned did not hit us for several days. When it did, each evening became more hilarious than the one before. It was now extremely unlikely that we should go to the Far East.

My hopes for an early release rose. Now that my services would not be required to defeat the Japs, what possible use could I be? It was inconceivable that the Military Authorities would be prepared to retain me at enormous expense to the taxpayer.

But keep me they did. Don't ask me why. I was a terrible officer. I was generally useless from drink through the hours of daylight, and always incapable in the evenings and nights. My ineptitude for soldiering must have been apparent to every member of the armed forces. My depradations of all supplies suitable for bartering were likely soon to cause an international scandal. My hatred of everything military was reaching psychopathic proportions, and it must have been obvious to all my superiors that to hold on to me for much longer could only result in a Court Martial, which would be a further waste of time for everyone concerned.

It was the day after John returned from leave that the blow fell. Major Windthrop had been away all day. I thought as I waved him good-bye at nine o'clock as I made my way to the Mess for a steadying pink gin that he looked somewhat grim.

John and I were discussing the international situation and our prospects in civvy street when Windy came in. From the look of thunder on his face I knew the news was bad.

I put a large whisky in his hand. 'Let's hear the worst.' I said.

Windy threw the whisky back in one gulp. 'The company disbands immediately. I have a home posting to War Office, God help me. You, John, will remain here for the winding up of the company. I have persuaded H.Q. to grant you the temporary rank of Major. Seeing as you're likely to have to face a Court Martial if anyone checks our stores and G.1098, I thought it the least I could do for you.'

'I refuse to call him "Sir," Windy,' I said.

Windy turned to me 'I don't know what there is about you, Michael. I did everything I could to persuade the silly buggers at H.Q. to let you go, but they're adamant. It's almost as if someone has said, "We need Nelson". Anyway, accept my condolences and a posting to a G.T. Company at Bari.'

When he had finished imparting further information to the other officers he concluded by saying: 'And now let the party begin'.

It was a good party. It was a monumental party. It lasted forty-eight hours, during which every officer, Warrant Officer, Non-Commissioned Officer and Driver reached a state of such inebriation that few could distinguish daylight from darkness.

When the battle was over the camp was a sorry sight. The beaches of Salerno looked as if they had been passed over by a mighty army in full retreat. Abandoned and burned tents lay buried in the sand. Here the charred hulk of a D.U.K.W. lay just beyond the waves. There a few bodies crawled among the dunes moaning piteously for water for the love of Allah.

With verbal lashes and physical ones with his swagger stick, the Company Sergeant-Major paraded the company, dressed them down for the last time, collapsed on the sand, was helped to his feet by two Sergeants, and continued to call every man jack on that parade an idle fucking soldier, unworthy of carrying the badge of the most honourable corps in the British Army. Bringing the parade to attention, he ordered a Present Arms, did a smart about turn, stumbled, regained his balance, threw up a salute to Windy, and fell to the ground again, still with his right hand to his peaked cap. From this horizontal position he called for three cheers for Major Windthrop.

I left the parade ground with tears in my eyes, and was glad to see a couple trickle down Windy's cheeks.

Two days later I drove with Driver Tibbs, who had been posted with me, into a grim-looking former Italian barracks at Bari, and reported to the Major commanding the General Transport Company.

No sooner had I saluted than I knew all was not well. I was an old soldier now, and my nostrils could smell trouble a mile off.

Major Taylor looked up from a heap of army forms he was signing, and studied me as if I were a nasty insect.

'Get out. Come back when you're properly dressed,' he bellowed.

Still suffering from the effects of the farewell party at Salerno, this unreasonable tone made me jump.

'Get out!'

I retired outside to lick my wounds. I could see I had a very real problem on my hands. I didn't like the sight of the Palestine medal on Major Taylor's chest. Those damned medals always spelt trouble, as if their recipients had been scarred mentally for life by the Arabs and the Jews shooting at them from both sides. Nor did I like Major Taylor's accent. I met some charming ex-ranker officers during the war, but when they were bastards they were real bastards. Here I had got one from very much the wrong side of the sheets.

I made my way to my extremely uncomfortable concrete room where I had told Driver Tibbs to stow my gear. As soon as I went in I could see that all was not well with Tibbs either.

'Here, Sir, what kind of a fucking mob have we landed up in?' he demanded agressively. 'The other batman who has turned up with another officer tells me that I'm expected to go on parade every morning.'

Batmen in my experience had always been excused such activities. It was one of the perks of the job.

Seeing another officer's camp bed in the room I asked: 'Who is it?'

'A Mr. Mackenzie, Sir.'

'I wonder if it could be young Mac who was at O.C.T.U. with me?' I said.

'I couldn't care less about that, Sir. All I know is we've got to get shifted out of here as quick as greased lightning.'

I sat down in the only available chair, eased off my boots and said 'These need a clean, Driver.'

Driver Tibbs looked at me as if I were mad. 'I cleaned them five days ago.'

'That's the point, Driver Tibbs. Major Taylor remarked on the fact. While you're about it, you'd better press my K.D. The trousers and the jacket.'

'I must be bloody dreaming,' said Driver Tibbs. 'Now look, Sir, you won't let me go on the morning parade will you? I mean I haven't got any bloody equipment. Oh my God, that reminds me, I left my bleedin' rifle at Salerno.'

'There's only one penalty for losing your best friend and that's a Court Martial and that means five years in the glasshouse.'

'They'd have to catch me first.'

'By the way, I noticed the Major was eyeing my medals with suspicion. You haven't sewn on the wrong ones, or maybe Driver Lane did. I'm not sprouting a V.C. to which I'm not entitled, am I by any chance?'

Driver Tibbs turned the jacket over. 'Looks like the usual fruit salad to me, Sir. Bit grimy, if you get my meaning.'

'Bit winey, you mean, Driver. I'd have you know I'm an old soldier and those medals have had more than one bottle spilt down them.'

'Looks to me as if the mice have been at them. I'll give 'em a clean up, Sir, don't you worry.'

While Driver Tibbs was making me a suitable person to be admitted to Major Taylor's presence, I put on my spare K.D. and made my way out onto the enormous square. I took a quick look round, and all my worst fears were confirmed. There were red fire buckets everywhere; lengths of rope painted white or blancoed such as I had not seen since leaving England three years before; the drivers and N.C.O.'s hurried across the square like scalded cats anxious to be off it as soon as possible; at the main gates were a couple of Regimental Police with swagger sticks dressed up like guardsmen outside Windsor Castle. In fact there was an extremely strong odour of bullshit emanating from every pore in the place.

I was about to go in search of the Company Sergeant-Major in pursuit of further bad news, if it were possible, when I heard a voice behind me call out, 'Mr Nelson, Sir.'

I turned and saw Sergeant James, who had looked after me in Major Hawkins' company, hurrying towards me. As he came up to me and saluted I saw that he carried the insignia of a Warrant Officer Class Two on his wrist.

'So you made it at last, Sergeant-Major,' I said.

'More than you've bloody done,' he answered smiling and looking at my two pips. 'Oh my God, Sir, you should never have come here. It's the most terrible place in the whole bloody world. You're not going to like it, Sir.'

'How did you end up here?'

'Bit of bad luck. When the war finished I got a touch of malaria, and Major Hawkins went off with his mob to Greece to deal with the communists or some other silly buggers. You'd have thought there'd been enough war in the world to be going on with. Anyway, I got made up to C.S.M. and sent here, and frankly, Sir, I'm thinking of jacking it in and reverting to Lance-Corporal.'

'How long have you got to serve?'

'I reckon another year. Plenty of service but a bit light on age.'

'Before I forget. I assume my batman can be excused morning parade?'

'More than my life's worth. Even the drivers on early morning detail have to parade first. Full kit, rifles, the whole bloody lot.'

'What's the company doing?'

'Feeding what's left of the army in these parts, and carrying grub for the civilians at the same time. Oh yes, there's a bit of ammo still coming into the docks.'

'That should be useful,' I said.

'I must be getting on my way, Sir. Major's inspection in an hour's time; the silly sods round here don't seem to have caught on that it's peace-time soldiering from now on. I'm afraid they got into bad ways when the war was on.' He paused. 'I don't mind telling you I wish it still was.'

When he had saluted he added: 'If you get depressed in the evenings you're welcome at the Sergeants' Mess, Sir. I think you'll like the lads, and they are all partial to a glass.'

Half an hour later in a state of extreme depression I knocked on Major Taylor's door and presented myself for his inspection.

'I want you to get one thing straight, Nelson,' he said. 'The war may be over, but you're still in the army. I propose to have a disciplined company operating in these barracks. In all my twenty years service never have I seen such a shower. I'm relying on you and Mackenzie to see that everything is up to my high standards. Understood?'

I could not bring myself to answer.

'Are you deaf, Nelson?'

'Listen, Major . . .'

'Call me, Sir . . .'

'Listen, Major,' I persisted. 'I had to spend the duration in the army, and I managed to spend most of it avoiding cunts like you. I don't intend . . .'

Major Taylor went red in the face. Leaning across his desk he hissed at me. 'Ah, so that's the way you want it is it?'

'That's the way I want it.'

'I see I've got a barrack-room lawyer to deal with. No witnesses to your subordination are there? So that's your little game. You can take it from me, Nelson, that I'm gunning for you from this minute, and I'll bloody well get you. To start with I'll have you on the square at two o'clock this afternoon, along with Mackenzie. He's another Bolshie one, and if it's the last thing I do I'll make a soldier of you.'

'Many have tried, and all have failed,' I said.

'Get out. Two o'clock on the square. F.M.O.'

In a suicidal mood I made enquiries for the Officers' Mess and made my way towards it, wondering how I could get the better of Major Taylor. I knew I had to be careful. Peacetime soldiering had returned with a vengeance, and I knew that there were plenty of officers like him sitting around with nothing to do except look forward to taking Summaries of Evidence or Court Martialling bolshies like me.

I was slightly cheered to find my old friend Mackenzie with whom I had attended O.C.T.U. in Bristol in 1941, standing in the mess when I walked in. I say Mess. It was more like a condemned cell. There was a concrete floor with no carpet on it, no sign of a bar, no decorations on the walls, and a nasty trestle table set up in the centre of the room on which had been laid out three tin plates and issue knives and forks.

Seeing the look of disgust on my face Mac said: 'Sorry, Michael, but it's worse than it looks. Welcome to Belsen.'

'Where's the bar?' I demanded.

'There's no drink. Major Taylor doesn't approve of young officers drinking. Don't forget we're still subalterns, and we're not entitled to speak while he shovels his food down.'

'Let's get to hell out of here. There must be somewhere decent to eat and drink in Bari.'

'Sorry, old chap. But we're not allowed out until the evenings. We spend a full working day here.'

'I must have a drink. I'm dying,' I said.

'Come across to the billet. I've got a bottle of Scotch in my kit,' said Mac.

As we walked across the square to our dismal room Mac filled me in with all his news. He had not gone to the 8th Army end in the Middle East but had landed with the First Army in North Africa, and had come on from there to Italy, having taken part in the landings at Salerno.

The more he told me about Major Taylor and life at Bari the more depressed I became. Thoughts of desertion crossed my mind.

'The trouble is we're the only two officers the sod's got and that means we have to do everything. Orderly Officer every other night. Which reminds me, Michael, when you've been Orderly Officer, when did you last turn out the guard?'

'I think back in England, when I was with Major Hawkins. Gave up all that rubbish long ago.'

'Not here you won't. Major Taylor checks with the Corporal in charge of the guard. Don't forget you're expected to be on morning parade with the first details before they leave camp. I suppose you'll tell me too you haven't carried out a vehicle inspection since 1942.'

'How did you guess?'

'You will here. Oh, you're going to love this place, Yes, into your denims first thing after the parade, and underneath those trucks you go.'

'I've forgotten what they look like from that angle.'

Young Mac began to laugh. He took a bottle of Scotch from under his bed and filled a glass for me.

'Now I've got news for you,' I said. 'It's square bashing for you and me at 1400 hours in F.M.O. I'll kill the sod if it's last thing I do.'

'You'd better hurry. The whole barracks is gunning for him. Seriously Michael, I think you'd better watch out. He's really nasty and I fear he's got a whiff of your reputation.'

'What do you mean by that?'

'It's got around, you know. I mean you don't exactly have a reputation in Italy for sobriety and soldiering.'

'The fact that my military genius has gone unrecognized has been a matter of bad luck.'

Half an hour later we entered the Mess to be greeted by Major Taylor demanding why we were late.

'As far as I'm concerned dinner is a parade. In future you will be here at 1300 hours, or rather five minutes before. I gather Nelson is a friend of yours, Mackenzie. Maybe he'll listen to you. Perhaps you'd inform him that I'm not going to be buggered about by a scruffy lieutenant whose pips are barely dry.'

'As a matter of fact I'm the longest serving lieutenant in the wartime British Army,' I said.

There was no further conversation during the meal, which was plain if edible, having come from the same cookhouse as the men's. Major Taylor decided to ignore us, and contented himself with shovelling the food into his mouth, making more noise than was necessary in the process.

At 1330 he stood up from the table and announced, 'I trust you are aware of the time. May I remind you that I expect you on parade in twenty-five minutes?'

When he had left the Mess Mac said, 'I don't think you should insult him like that. It only makes him worse.'

'I didn't know that was possible. Come on let's go and get dressed up like a couple of Christmas trees.'

When I emerged from our billet looking the most slovenly turned out officer possible, Mac feared for my safety. Naturally I had no rifle, only a .38 pistol which had become corroded by the ozone of Salerno. This was attached to my belt, and that was the full extent of my F.M.O. I had no large or small pack, Driver Lane having decided many years ago that they were accoutrements of little use to an officer in his journey through the Middle East, Sicily and Italy.

Although I knew I could not beat Major Taylor at his game, I was angry and had determined to irritate him to the maximum, bearing in mind that there was a limit over which I should not drive him. Accordingly when he asked me as we arrived on parade where the rest of my equipment was I told him quite untruthfully that it had been lost in the final push against the Germans when I had been serving with the Armoured Brigade. For some reason this seemed to satisfy him, and he ordered me to report to the C.Q.M.S. Stores, get myself fully kitted out and report back on parade at 1800 hours.

Taking Mac's advice I did as I was ordered, but I must confess that after I had been drilled with Mac for an hour that evening on the square by Major Taylor, I came very close to breaking point. I honestly believe that if I had had a bayonet attached to the end of my newly issued rifle I might well have stuck it through Major Taylor's guts. I was out of my mind with fury at having come full circle. I had been bullied on the square four years before when I had been called up. Then I had been able to see the point of it all. Millions of men had to be trained and knocked into shape as quickly as possible during a time of emergency. Now it was senseless, absolutely unreasonable.

I was with that General Transport Company in Bari for about six weeks. It was only thanks to Mac's advice that I managed to keep out of serious trouble. Nor was there a great deal of time for relaxation.

Every morning I was on the parade with the two platoons, both of whom I had to inspect, before handing them over to Major Taylor's mercy. Afterwards it was my job to inspect the vehicles that were off the road for the day, and fill in numerous paragraphs about the health of their back axles and other mechanical mysteries. All this had to be done in the heat of the Southern Italian summer and the never-ceasing attacks of the Italian flies.

In the afternoons there was no siesta. This was a luxury not approved of by Major Taylor. Instead I set out on a motor-cycle to see that those of the drivers who were carting rations and petrol round the countryside, were doing their job properly and not trading with the local population. In fact, they were completely brow-beaten and utterly honest. The Major had set up a highly efficient system of check points which, allied to a fleet of mobile N.C.O.'s on motor-cycles, had stamped out all profitable enterprise.

That G.T. Company was the most miserable one with which it was my misfortune to serve. It's easy to tell when a company is happy. There is an absence of defaulters outside the Orderly Room each morning. Every morning at Bari there was a parade of at least a dozen men. This was in spite of the fact that C.S.M. James and his N.C.O.'s were all very unhappy with the situation. The trouble was that Major Taylor was one of those unpleasant soldiers who had the knack of being everywhere at the same time. Woe betide an N.C.O. who failed to charge a driver for the most paltry offence, like dropping a cigarette end on the barrack square, or spitting into one of the fire buckets. Somehow Major Taylor was always there to see the offence being committed.

The only relief from this disastrous situation was either plotting to murder Major Taylor, or taking refuge in the Sergeants' Mess on the nights when I was not Orderly Officer. I was safe there because Major Taylor had never been invited to the Sergeants' Mess, nor was he ever likely to be, and would on no account so much as think of putting a foot inside without first being asked. Such was the protocol which as an N.C.O. himself before the war he had learned to love and observe.

Luckily, in spite of the Major's dislike of the stuff, the Sergeants' Mess was well stocked with all kinds of drink. To begin with they all insisted on buying me drinks, but after a few days I took the C.S.M. to one side, confided in him that I was a rich man thanks to Driver Lane, and would like to pay my own way.

C.S.M. James remembered Driver Lane well from the day he had first come to me as a batman in England. 'I'm glad he turned out all right financially,' he commented. 'The worst bloody soldier in the whole of Major Hawkins' company, and that's going some.'

As a result of this understanding I was able to stand my own round in the Sergeants' Mess, which seemed the only fair thing to do as, owing to the strong enforcement of military discipline on Major Taylor's part, they were all drawing their army pay to a man.

It was shortly after this that I was making my way to the Mess for my lunch time swill that I was nearly knocked over by a Jeep which had come through the main gates at high speed. At the wheel was my friend Captain John Fish, or rather Major Fish, having been promoted to wind up the D.U.K.W. Company at Salerno.

I leapt into the Jeep and asked him what he was doing in Bari.

'Posted to this mob, Michael,' he said.

'Oh no, anything but that, John. It's worse than you've heard.'

'Ah, is that so? Then perhaps I won't come after all. I'm not due here for two days, so I thought I'd come over and take a dekko and get the low down before putting myself at risk.'

'John, do anything but come here. Rape your sister, shoot the General, but on no account get posted here. You know what's written over the barrack entrance? "Abandon hope all ye who enter here".'

'I heard over at Salerno that you weren't too happy. What about a drink?'

'I've got a bottle hidden under my bed.'

John whistled aloud. 'How are the mighty fallen!'

When we had driven to my room and I had opened my last bottle of Scotch, which was getting in very short supply, I poured out my tale of woes to John.

'Definitely not the place for me,' he commented when I had finished. 'Right, we'd better get you out of it too before you run into serious trouble.'

'How?'

'Come and jump out of aeroplanes with me.'

'Do what?'

'Exactly as I say. Look, they want volunteers for the para Brigade.'

'But the war's over.'

'Exactly. They reckon the paras will be an important part of the peace-time army. That's why they're asking for volunteers. I've got a mate at G.H.Q. and he will get you posted for training if you give me the O.K.'

'I can't do it!' I said.

'You mean you are a coward and more terrified of having to jump out of a plane than go on facing the Major here?'

'I don't mind the jumping,' I said. 'I don't like it when the parachute fails to open.'

I was more tempted to join John than I pretended. When the time came to tell my children and grandchildren what I had done in the war, how much better it would sound to say I had been a paratrooper rather than a Driver in the Royal Army Service Corps. On the other hand as time passed one could say that anyway. I know someone high up in the B.B.C. who tells everyone he was a paratrooper. He doesn't know that I have met some of his old drivers who tell me that he was in command of a platoon in a G.T. company after the war, and was a rotten officer into the bargain.

I think John was disappointed at my refusal to join him and spend the next couple of months jumping out of planes. He must have thought from what he had heard of my predicament that I would need little persuasion.

So he drank my last bottle of Scotch with me and did nothing further to try to make me alter my mind. After which, declining to make the acquaintance of Major Taylor, he returned to his Jeep and drove off to see his friend at G.H.Q. to ensure that he should proceed directly to the para training battalion, and on no account have to dirty his boots with the dust of Bari.

Once again I could not help being impressed by the way John conducted his military life. Unlike me he always seemed to have friends in the right place. Whereas Major Hawkins had always put up with John's most outrageous behaviour, he had always been extra agile in stamping on the slightest deviation from duty on my part. You could have said of Captain John Fish that if you threw him into a cesspit he would come up smelling of violets.

I think, as I look back on the events of that late summer and early autumn in Bari, that Major Taylor must have slowly been going mad. It occurs to me now that he was displaying all the symptoms of acute megalomania mixed with an obsession for cleanliness. Students of Freud will attribute the latter to some incident in his childhood, some unfortunate accident with his chamber-pot or an obsessive infantile attachment to his own excreta. It started with cigarette ends. If he saw one lying on the ground in the barracks he would fly into a rage and order extra parades. The drivers just about put up with this, but when he started going red in the face at the sight of a used matchstick lying on the ground, they began to turn nasty.

On every side I heard mutterings. I even received a deputation complaining about the Major's behaviour and demanding that I do something about it. Knowing my King's Regulations, I could see that any move on my part could be interpreted as mutiny. Although the war was over and I would be unlikely to face a firing squad, I had no desire to end up in the glasshouse stripped of my two ancient pips. Accordingly I delivered the deputation a right bollocking with my tongue in my cheek and told them that if they came to me again with a complaint I would personally march them in front of the Major.

Among the deputation was a certain Driver Jones. That isn't his real name. I last met him seven years ago when he had come off the Moor where he had just completed seven years for robbery with violence. He is now back inside for a particularly nasty crime of the same kind. I hope he stays there because he is a menace to society. There is nothing I can say in extenuation of his behaviour. He is one of those people who have to be locked up because they have a natural bent for knocking innocent people on the head.

Driver Jones at the time was paying court to an Italian girl in Bari. As he was kept very busy parading for Major Taylor's benefit or driving his lorry, the time he could devote to his heart's desire was strictly limited.

One day Major Taylor was driving about the countryside on a motorcycle looking for drivers he could charge for speeding, smoking at the wheel, carrying civilian passengers, or other minor infringements of the military code and, seeing one of his trucks coming towards him, he dismounted and waved it to a halt.

At the wheel was Driver Jones. Commanded by the Major to step down from his cab, he did as he was told, and watched the Major carry out a search inside the front of the lorry.

The Major could find nothing about which he could complain. Suddenly with a roar he spied a cigarette-end lodged beneath the clutch pedal. Seizing upon this as evidence he immediately charged the Driver with smoking in W.D. Transport.

The next day Driver Jones was marched in front of the Major, and confined to barracks for ten days, added to which he was ordered to parade with the morning and evening guard kitted out in F.M.O.

I could sense that Driver Jones was planning vengeance. He became quiet and morose, so that the other drivers, who were already slightly frightened of him, avoided his company altogether.

He completed his sentence without any visible trouble, was marched before the Major by C.S.M. James, given a second dressing-down, and reminded that he was still in the army and any further slovenly behaviour on his part would incur a heavier sentence.

Driver Jones returned to driving his vehicle. I am not quite sure what make they were, but they had been handed over to the Company by the Americans. I know they were seven-tonners, really good trucks that put our own transport to shame. They were equipped with servo-assisted air brakes, which made a highly impressive hissing noise when applied and released.

I can remember the particular day when it happened very well. Much to Major Taylor's annoyance he had to allow me the afternoon off to have my teeth attended to in Bari. Naturally, after the dentist had done his worst, I lingered about the town, first of all drinking to get over the pain in a small cafe, and then moving on to the Officers' Club. It was not until ten o'clock that I returned to the barracks.

As soon as I had passed through the gates, I knew that something was wrong.

To begin with the square was full of drivers and N.C.O.'s. To my amazement they were all smoking, laughing and quite a number of them were the worse for vino.

They quietened a little as I made my way to the Mess.

There I found Mac looking green about the face. He gave me the news.

After lunch, soon after I had gone to see the dentist, Major Taylor had mounted his motor-bike and left the camp in search of defaulting drivers. He was never seen alive again.

He had been following a truck to check its speed. Suddenly its driver had braked hard to avoid a child that had run out into the road in front of it. In spite of its seven tons those brakes were far superior to the brakes of the motor-cycle.

Major Taylor had gone straight under the rear of the truck. On the way he lost his head. Later it was recovered lying among a field of grapes, and restored to the torso.

The driver of the truck under which Major Taylor lost his head was Driver Jones.

It was difficult to be appalled. I hated the man too much—but I have not the slightest doubt to this day that Major Taylor was murdered.

I mentioned my theory a few days later to my old friend C.S.M. James and I can remember exactly what he said: 'It's funny you should say that, Sir. Try as we can we haven't been able to trace the child that ran out into the road. Now what will you have, Sir? Large Scotch?'

I made the mistake of pressing my point: 'Do you think there was dirty work?'

'A large Scotch, wasn't it, Sir? Don't say anything more. There are some things that two pippers shouldn't know about. Let me put it this way, Sir. There are some things that fall off lorries, and there are some bastards that go under them. Coming up, Sir. One large Scotch with a drip of water.'

Chapter Eight

Two weeks after the death of Major Taylor, I came into the Officers'
Mess for lunch, and found there a strange Major. On his chest I noticed
a row of medals, among them the Palestinian Gong, and my heart sank.
Could it be that Major Taylor had departed this life, only to be replaced
by another Major of similar outlook?'

The new Major eyed me up and down. Looking round the Mess he
said: 'This is a disgrace. It's worse. It's a bloody pigsty. What'll you
have? I'm Major Lyons, by the way.'

'I'll have a gin, Sir.'

Mac and I, who had been running the company between us since
Major Taylor's death, had installed a supply of alcohol in the Mess,
although we had not yet got round to improving its food or decor.

'Anything with it?'

'Water please, Sir.'

'You Michael Nelson or Bob Mackenzie?'

'Nelson, Sir.'

'Christ, cut it out. This is not a bloody parade ground. My name's
Ben. How do you do?'

We shook hands. A sense of relief began to seep through my blood. I
downed my gin in one gulp and poured two more from the bottle.

'Where are the Mess servants?' demanded Major Lyons.

'I'm afraid we don't run to them. The late Major didn't approve of
that kind of thing. As a matter of fact they're not catered for on the
establishment.'

'Bugger the establishment. Look, I don't like pigging it, Michael.
Raise a couple of Mess servants. In fact on second thoughts I don't like
having the mess in these barracks one little bit. I'll have a word with the
Town Major who's a friend of mine and see about him getting us a
decent place outside.'

'I assume you've come to take over the company,' I said.

'That's the idea, I gather from the C.S.M. it's not exactly a happy
ship. The first thing to do is to see about altering that. How many
Officers have I got?'

'Two.'

'Then regard yourself as Mess President, Entertainments Officer,

Education Officer and any other bloody officer that happens to come to your mind.'

'What about Orderly Officer? You see, Mac and I have been doing Orderly Officer every other day.'

'That's out for a start. Count me in together with the C.S.M. How many Staff Sergeants have we got?'

'One'.

'Then the Sergeants will have to do their whack. It won't do them any harm to give up their nightly boozing once a week.' He paused. 'I expect you're wondering who the devil I am?'

'Not at all, Sir.'

'Don't bullshit me. I saw how you glanced at my rows of honourable fruit salad.'

'The M.C. is not salad,' I said.

'It came up with the rations. There weren't enough to go round the entire tank crew so the C.O. said I'd better have it. I was with the Hussars. As a matter of fact I seem to know more about you than you do about me. You served under Major Thompson in my old Armoured Brigade. You even once delivered a load of ammo to my tank, but you were too stoned to know what you were doing.'

'Then what are you doing here commanding a company of the R.A.S.C.?' I asked.

'The only way I could obtain a regular commission. Couldn't afford my own Regiment. In spite of what they say you need a private income in peacetime. I'm the son of a jobbing gardener in Kent, so you'll understand my problem. Don't get me wrong. I'm grateful to get a commission in the Corps. By the way, how long have you been a subaltern?'

'Since December, 1941.'

'Bloody ridiculous.'

'That's what I think. If I'd have had my way I would have been at least a full Colonel by now.'

A few days later I moved the Officers' Mess into a comfortable villa on the outskirts of Bari.

Before the war it had been the property of a local fascist official, who had spent a considerable amount of money on its decorations and furnishing. Of the latter little had survived the depredations of a succession of passing soldiers. All the moveable furniture had either been looted or chopped up for firewood. The wallpaper had suffered from the creative leanings of thwarted artists. Nymphs sprouted moustaches, angels had feathers sticking out of their orifices, while the satyrs boasted pricks the size of which would have made even them open their eyes in pride and wonder.

The most attractive room in the house was a small bar, the centre of which boasted a dance floor lit from below by a selection of coloured lights. It was here that Major Lyons established his mess, and it was here that I brought several loads of furniture, requisitioned from the surrounding houses of the rich. Needless to say they were extremely upset at seeing their furniture carried off. One can understand their feelings. It must have been particularly galling to see it disappear, after they had successfully hidden it during the war, and had only brought it out after peace had been declared when they had imagined it safe from the hands of the predatory military. I considered it bad luck and bad judgement on their part.

I imported Driver Tibbs and Mac's servant as Mess waiters, both of whom moved into the upper reaches of the house. From the cries of female protest that echoed down the corridors late at night, it would appear that they had quickly availed themselves of such female company as was available in the town. I contented myself with warning them of the dangers of V.D., to which Driver Tibbs commented that I was the one that ought to look out as I was so often pissed that it seemed unlikely that I would have the strength to avail myself of the protection of a French letter, let alone find my way to a prophylactic station.

There had been a high incidence of V.D. among all ranks during the Italian Campaign. The arrival of penicillin had increased the lust of the soldiery who imagined that here for the first time was a drug that would keep the disease of Venus at bay. Unfortunately it was not to be. News of the wonder drug permeated through the whores' and pimps' grapevine. Overnight penicillin became one of the most valued commodities on the Black Market. Every lady of easy virtue, both amateur and professional, hastened to avail herself of this magical cure. The result was inevitable. The streptococci and other bacteria quickly developed an immunity to the drug. Soon the sad day arrived when the soldier could no longer be guaranteed a speedy cure for his indulgence.

Although I was much better off now that I had been freed from the tyranny of Major Taylor, I was very unhappy. My own thoughts failed to turn to love, and I entered upon a period of melancholy, which heavy libations did nothing to alleviate. One can reach a point in drinking when drunkenness produces only misery prior to oblivion. I found too that *the* glass was descending more and more quickly. *The* glass is something that drinkers will understand. One can go on drinking without falling down or entering into a state of intoxication until one comes to *the* glass. After that glass all is lost. Drunks through history have been trying to pin-point that glass, to calculate exactly when it will come up. If only they could do this they would never become incapable through drink. If only one could pause before *the* glass, draw back, and wait a while, one could then carry on boozing until such a time as *the* glass would once again rear its ugly head.

It was at this period in Bari that for the first time I began to think seriously about what was going to happen to me when the army finally decided that I was of no further use to it. I wondered if I could return to journalism; I considered putting in an application to go up to a university but quickly rejected the idea when I realized that it would mean subjecting myself to a further period of discipline. I no longer thought of myself as a writer, least of all as a poet who had something to offer the world. Much more was I conscious of my worthlessness. Much as I longed to return to civvy street and to be free from military discipline, the more I considered the possibilities the less inviting the future became. I found that whenever I considered the problem of the future I quickly exhausted all the possibilities and the easiest answer was to return to a full glass. I was not silly enough to imagine that I had solved any problems. It was a method of postponing having to face up to them.

The truth of the matter was that the army had sapped my will power, had taught me not to think for myself. I had failed to take what few benefits it could have offered me. Besides too much alcohol I had indulged in too much self-pity.

It was here too in Bari that for the first time that I began to develop not only an anxiety neurosis about my future but a real fear for it. It was here, as I reeled to my bed late at night, that I first told myself that if I could not find the answer, there at least remained to me the right to kill myself.

One evening, when I was drinking with Major Lyons, he reopened the subject of my rank, or rather my lack of it. He seemed fascinated that after so many years I had not graduated beyond the rank of subaltern. I tried to demonstrate to him by stories of my past behaviour that this was inevitable.

'You must have served under some right bastards,' he commented.

'No. Under some conscientious ones,' I replied. 'I'm afraid the trouble, Ben, is that not only have I not been able to take soldiering seriously, I haven't even been able to *look* serious about it. Add to that the fact that I loathe arse creepers, not to mention my cowardice, drunkenness and inefficiency, and you will come to the conclusion that it's nothing less than a miracle that I even managed to progress beyond the rank of Driver.'

Ben shook his head. 'There must be something good about you, somewhere Michael. No one can be so absolutely rotten as you make yourself out to be.'

I shook my head sadly. 'Ben, you are a wonderful man and I appreciate your efforts at kindness. But this poor soldier will die happy if he can secure an honourable discharge.'

'Would you have liked to have been a Captain?'

'I would have liked it for my mother's sake, possibly for my father's but above all for Driver Lane's. But alas it's too late for him now. I imagine he has now returned to the Old Country and is back in civvy street. I shall always remember the look of reproach in his eyes when subalterns much junior to me turned up sprouting their three pips and started to order me about. He found it far more humiliating than I did. I suppose too that I should like to put another pip up in case I should run into my old friend John Fish again. It would be worth seeing the look of utter amazement and disbelief on his face, beside the fact that I am on to a fiver to twenty with him that I will make it before I finally leave the army. The thought of losing another fiver to him is one of the hardest and most depressing burdens that this poor subaltern has to bear.'

Two days after this conversation with Major Lyons, I was wakened from my siesta by Driver Tibbs bearing tea and brandy and a message from Major Lyons that I was to dine in Mess that evening without fail even if it meant absenting myself from the delights of the bar of the Officers' Club in Bari and the embraces of the local enchantresses.

After a bath, I climbed into my best evening wear consisting of K.D. desert boots somewhat worn round the uppers, and a bright blue and yellow scarf, the one which had offended the Provost Corps some weeks earlier in Udine. Although, now that we were back to peacetime, I did not sport this old desert gear in public for fear of reprimand by some regular in pursuit of promotion which was becoming increasingly elusive now that the part-time soldiers were returning to civvy street and hard built empires were crumbling right and left, Major Ben Lyons had no objection to my wearing it in his Mess.

In the Mess I found Ben Lyons and young Mac already assembled, drinking some rather nasty champagne. Although my efforts since the death of Major Taylor had been fully devoted to stocking the bar of the Mess rather than parading on the square for his benefit, and I had been able to lay in an ample stock of the usual run of spirits and some drinkable wines which the ex-fascists had recently dug up from their secret hiding places just at the right time for me to slap a requisition order on them, I had failed to locate any French champagne. Bari is after all a long way down to the south of Italy and a fair old distance from Rheims.

By the look of Ben and Mac it seemed that they had gone in for quantity and ignored the quality. They were both in a decidedly giggly mood.

In order not to appear offensive I accepted the champagne they poured for me. I found that after the first bottle the second bottle tasted slightly better, and so on, so that by the fifth by closing one's eyes one could imagine that one's lips were sipping a vintage Veuve Cliquot or Krug.

I must have been into bottle number three, possibly four, when I heard Major Lyons say: 'Here's to you both. Good luck, Captain Mackenzie and Captain Nelson.'

'That's almost in worse taste than this piss called champagne,' I remarked.

'It's true, Michael,' said Mac. 'We are both to be promoted to the rank of Captain.'

Then I heard the full story.

Ben Lyons had been incensed by the treatment of both Mac and myself. We had both passed out of O.C.T.U. together, and according to Ben it had been wrong of the army to fail to promote us. He was not suggesting for one minute that we should have been promoted on merit. But there was such a thing as seniority, and as a regular soldier seniority counted for a lot. It was entirely due to the fact that we had in the past been commanded by civilians rather than regulars, that our seniority together with the rights it carried, had been so wrongfully ignored. Civilians might be all right in war time, but they were sometimes over-keen, wanted to see too many results, and at times were taken in by the wiles of other arse-creeping temporary soldiers.

Later in the evening I discovered how Ben Lyons had performed this double miracle.

Like all regular soldiers, he had a great many friends in the army. One of these had long ago transferred to the R.A.S.C. not being smart enough for a commission in his own regiment. He had reached the rank of Brigadier, and on hearing that he was at Naples, Ben Lyons had driven over to see him. Calling upon the old pals' act, and threatening to expose him for something that had occurred in the horse lines before the war in India, he had bullied him into promoting both Mac and me.

Three days later Mac departed north to join an infantry division in Austria, where it was said to be standing by in a state of constant alert to oppose the Russian hordes, who having fooled all the western politicians, were now threatening to take over the whole of Europe.

The following day, having said good-bye to Major Lyons, I set out once again to cross Italy to join an Italian Civilian Transport Company with the rank of Captain. Driver Tibbs went with me. I am glad he was more insensitive than Driver Lane, who would have been quick to remark that I could not sink much lower than to join an Italian Civilian mob, even if it was the only method whereby I could reach the exalted rank of Captain. The fact that it was operating on the outskirts of Salerno would no doubt have prompted some further humiliating comment from him.

So the Autumn of 1945 found me once again back near the beaches of Salerno.

After enquiring of the local population we discovered that the company was situated just outside the town. A few minutes later Driver Tibbs drew up our fifteen-hundredweight at the entrance to the camp, and was very amused when I was saluted by a scruffy Italian who was acting as a guard on the gate. He seemed to show no resentment at being a member of a beaten nation, but cheerfully grinned away between salutes and told us that we could find the Officers' Mess and the Maggiore up at the villa. Accordingly we proceeded as directed. On either side of the drive I noticed standings for vehicles, and here and there the odd truck which looked decidedly the worse for wear. You can always tell transport that belongs to the British Army. However ancient and obsolescent its design, at least it looks as if someone cares for it. The transport of all other nations, especially of those whose shores border the Mediterranean, always looks semi-derelict. This is usually true as the people concerned treat their trucks very badly, and are prone to sell off odd parts for vast profits in the local bazaars.

When we finally reached the villa, I was once again confronted by a brigand armed with the helm of an axe. When I dismounted from the truck, he made a poor show of presenting arms with it, as he burst into an incomprehensible Neapolitan dialect, the only word of which I could recognize was 'Capitano'.

It seemed to me quite extraordinary that a member of the Italian race, which had shown such keenness in shedding its arms in time of war, should now be so anxious to play at soldiers. But as Marlene Dietrich sang: 'When will they ever learn?'

Even Driver Tibbs, who fancied himself as a linguist, and had picked up a fair smattering of the lingo from his courting days, failed to understand the stream of words.

We were finally rescued by the appearance of a Sergeant of the Corps who emerged from the building, looking bleary-eyed. It was clear to me that he had been disturbed from a late siesta.

Seeing my three pips he saluted and said: 'It must be Captain Nelson, Sir. Welcome to this shower of shit. You look tired, Sir. No doubt you and your driver could do with a cup of tea or possibly something stronger. My name is Sergeant Wright, Sir.'

I followed Sergeant Wright into the villa and he led the way to the Sergeants' Mess.

'There's only myself and Sergeant Crouch,' he explained as he filled three glasses of wine from a litre bottle.

The wine was very good and I said so.

'Don't worry, Sir, nothing but the best here. You only have to tell these thieving Eyties what you want, and it'll be on your table in a few hours. I honestly believe if you asked them to deliver the Queen Mary to the bay of Salerno they would manage to find some way of getting her there. Frankly, Sir, they frighten the life out of me. What they're up to is nobody's business. I thought I knew a thing or two about fiddling, but these bastards beat me hollow.'

In the course of further conversation I gathered that the Company employed Italian civilian drivers because of the shortage of drivers in the Corps. The role of the company was obscured. It serviced the few remaining units of the Allied Army in the vicinity. These were mostly base troops who were still looking after ammunition, ordnance and supply dumps, which would now never be required. It seemed to me extraordinary that these vast dumps were still in an area over which the war has passed two years previously.

It appeared that the civilian drivers were little interested in the job for which they had been engaged. All that mattered to each one of them was to get their hands on a lorry. Civilian transport was still non-existent and the owner of a lorry could earn himself a fortune every week by working for civilian contractors. With a staff of two Sergeants, one Major, myself and one other Captain who was in charge of workshops, it was only possible to keep an eye on a very small number of the drivers.

According to Sergeant Wright one did a magnificent job if one prevented the drivers from flogging their lorries when they had amassed enough wealth with which to retire.

Sergeant Wright ended on a stern note of warning: 'If you want to get out of this mob alive, I shouldn't be too hard on them, Sir. I don't know much about it but I expect you've heard of the Mafia. I'm pretty sure they've won control of this lot. Don't run foul of old Pietro. He's the boss round here, and what he says goes.'

'What about the Major?'

'Very decent fellow, Sir. Like us all, wants to get demobbed in one piece. Besides I reckon he's a bit loose in the head. Spends all his time at the opera in Naples. A bit of a queer one if you ask me, Sir. But no trouble at all. It's this bloody Mafia you've got to worry about.'

In the last two years I had heard various stories about the Mafia. In those days they were not reckoned much of a power. Prior to the invasion of Sicily the Americans, in their usual innocent way, had shipped some Mafia agents from the United States into the island to act as secret agents and stir the populace to acts of violence against the fascists and the Germans and generally to lend a hand to the liberating forces when they landed.

This stupidity on the part of the Americans had turned out a sick joke. All that had happened was that the criminals had set about feathering their nests and imposing their rule of violence on the wretched Sicilian peasants, thereby laying the foundations of the modern Sicilian Mafia which keeps a stranglehold on that poverty-stricken island to this day.

The trouble with the Americans is that they're still a young and in-experienced nation. They fall into the error of believing in the inherent goodness of human nature. They committed the same error in Europe after the war. It is thanks to their interference and belief that the U.S.S.R. could not really be as nasty as their better-informed Allies kept telling them, that half of Europe now suffers beneath the injustices of so-called communism.

I left Sergeant Wright and, as I made my way to the Officers' Mess, I could not help wondering whether my third pip was going to prove worthwhile.

In the Mess I found a weary-looking Captain thumbing through an old copy of the *Illustrated London News*.

'I'm Bill Crump,' he said. 'Welcome to this madhouse.'

'I'm beginning to wonder if I should ever have come here.'

'Nothing to wonder about, old boy. This is a complete and utter nuthouse. Still, I've only a couple of months to go till I get out of the army. I think I'll have to slip away under cover of darkness. Do you know what those buggers have gone and done last night? Gone and flogged the last lathe in working order. By the way, I'm the Workshops Officer for my sins. What did you do to get sent here? Rape the General's daughter? Flog a Liberty ship? They always say criminals make the best gaolers. Help yourself to a drink. It's all free by the way. We tried to pay for it but the buggers think we're mad, or else that we don't like it. Tried to refuse a case of Haig the other day, so they came back with some Johnny Walker. Have you met Major Miller? Terrible fellow; I should keep clear of him. Got a touch of the sun if you ask me. Spends all his time listening to music or a lot of idiots caterwauling away in the opera house. Mad as a hatter. Don't think he's spoken to me since I arrived.

'Where is he now?'

'God knows. Probably down in the harbour getting an eyeful of the fisherboys. There's a German truck company down the road and when the moon's full he walks up and down outside returning their salutes. Had the audacity to invite one of the Hun officers up for a drink the other night. I told him straight that I would have liked to have shot the bugger. Do you know what he said? 'Beauty, dear boy, is in the eye of the beholder.' What the hell he meant by that I haven't the faintest idea.' He stood up. 'Well, I suppose I'd better get back to my workshops or rather what's left of them and post some so-called sentries for the night.'

It seemed to me that Captain Bill Crump was himself as mad as a hatter, whatever his opinion of Major Miller.

I poured myself a large whisky.

The door opened and Major Miller swept into the room. Immediately I realized what Sergeant Wright had meant by referring to him as a bit of a queer one. Bill Crump's remarks should have put me wise.

Major Geoffrey Miller advanced towards me with outstretched arms. As I held out one hand he seized it with both of his. They were cool and soft and, looking down, I noticed the immaculately manicured nails, and unless my eyes deceived me they were painted with a touch of nail varnish.

He was wearing one of the most splendid outfits of K.D. that I had ever seen, made of silk that gave off a sheen as he moved. The shirt was of a pale brown silk and the tie was to match. I noticed that his jacket was held in round his waist by a belt of silk. Even his shoes were unusual. I could not determine at a glance exactly what they were, but they were made of no ordinary calves' leather.

'Welcome, my dear Captain Nelson,' he said looking me straight in the eyes. His own I noticed were of the palest blue. His lips were full and pouted like a cupids. His eyebrows were thin, and had been plucked, and there wafted from him a smell of scent.

He must have seen my nostrils move for he exclaimed: 'So you noticed it. That's a good sign, my dear Captain. Chanel No 5. Sometimes I risk Jicky, and on special occasions Mitzoukou.'

'Diaghilev's favourite,' I said.

For a moment I thought that he would explode with joy. 'No, no, I can't believe it. I won't believe it. You're not another moron then. That's all they send me. Moron after moron waiting for their demobilization. So called officers like the dreadful Crump. Crump, my dear. How could one ever talk with a man called Crump. So you adore the ballet, do you?'

Before I could answer he had clapped his hands. A waiter dressed in a white jacket appeared in the doorway and he said, 'A bottle of champagne, my dear, and do make sure it's not warm.'

When the waiter retired he turned to me and said, 'My dear Michael, for I'm going to call you Michael, I can see at once that you're sympatico. We are going to have the most marvellous time here together. God has answered a maiden's prayer at last. I shall call at the Duomo tomorrow and light lots of candles to the Holy Virgin.'

Major Miller paused to cross himself.

'A most beautiful cathedral. You will simply adore the paschal and the tomb of Margaret of Anjou. There's also a Pope, Gregory VII, but I'm afraid he's not very gay. Now tell me all you know about the ballet? What about Freddie Ashton? How is the dear thing?'

'I'm afraid I've been overseas for over three years and am rather out of touch with the art world.'

'And that Bobbie Helpmann? He must pack it in soon or he'll have a coronary. Now don't be secretive. Tell me all the people you know in London, and I will tell you all mine. Oh, this is such fun. Can you imagine me having a cosy chat with that dreadful Crump? My dear, I've been starved, literally starved of civilized people for months and months.'

'I hope you won't be disappointed in me, Major. I'm afraid I've become a bit of a philistine and a drunkard into the bargain.'

He waved a finger at me. 'Naughty, naughty Nellie. I know all about you, don't forget. Broke lots and lots of hearts at the Café Royal before the war, didn't we?'

'You're confusing me with someone else.'

'Now, now, there's nothing to be ashamed of. We have our sources of information, don't we? It's very naughty of you to take to the bottle. So utterly ruinous to the complexion.' He leant forward and examined my face closely. 'Dearie, dearie me, what an awful lot of grog blossoms. Tut, tut. Take my advice, my dear, and keep off the spirits or else I shall be forced to call you Captain Blossom, and you wouldn't like that would you?'

The waiter brought in the champagne and put it on the table.

'Would you care to open it, dear boy?' asked Major Miller.

'Go ahead, Major.'

'Now lets get something straight, dear boy. Not Major, but Geoffrey. On no account Geoff. I think the abbreviation of Christian names is excessively vulgar. You know, Pete for Peter. How would you like Mike for Michael? After all Michael was a Saint and a very grand one at that.'

He literally waltzed round the table so that I could appreciate his figure held tightly in by the silk belt round his waist. He didn't miss much. Seeing that I was looking at him he performed a pirouette and said, 'Not bad for thirty-two you have to admit. If I may say so I think you really ought to do something about your weight. You look much too much like a baby elephant, my dear. And you cannot be more than 24 if you're a day.'

'Twenty-three.'

Geoffrey Miller tut-tutted three times. 'Naughty, naughty. As your commanding officer I'm ordering you to drink nothing but wine while you're under my command. Promise me? I think you're going to find me a very charming commanding officer and we could have lots and lots of fun together.'

'It all sounds very amusing,' I said, 'but what will my duties be?'

'To entertain me,' said Geoffrey giving me a wink. 'Seriously, there is very little to do here. The company more or less runs itself and I leave the Italians to get on with it.'

I was surprised at this remark considering what Sergeant Wright and Bill Crump had told me. 'I know I've only been here a couple of hours, Geoffrey,' I said, 'but I gather that the Italians are not as honest as they should be.'

'How silly you are. Who's ever heard of an honest Italian? My dear, they would pick the pockets of their best friend. That reminds me. Have you heard what they're up to in Naples? Well, my dear, the dear old mummies are carting their babies about in baskets on their heads, and have trained these babies to put out a hand and steal the hats off the passers by. Isn't that too clever for words? How well do you know Naples? Such a wicked, wicked city. I very much look forward to being your official guide. My dear, Piccadilly has absolutely nothing on the Galleria. Of course one really needs a taste for *nostalgie de la boue* to appreciate the true flavour of the Neapolitans. For me they're just a little bit too grubby if ever so naughty. I must confess I prefer the Aryan type. Which reminds me, there's rather an interesting P.O.W. camp just down the road which I am sure would be worth our investigating.'

138

Geoffrey had now removed the cork from the champagne bottle and proceeded to fill two fluted glasses.

I raised my glass: 'Good health,' I said. 'I hope I'm going to be happy here. I'm still a little worried about what I have to do.'

'I've told you. Entertain me during my last few weeks of *la vie militaire*.'

'It's all very well for you. What'll happen to me when you've gone and someone in authority finds that the Eyties have flogged all the lorries?'

Geoffrey became serious for a moment. 'There's nothing to worry about. You see, I took over this company from my predecessor without signing for a single nut or bolt, let alone a truck or the workshop section. Everyone is being demobilized so fast that there's no time for a proper handover. It's the same at H.Q. in Naples. No one there has the faintest idea what's happening. They don't even know what the units under their command are supposed to be doing. As I see it the sooner we all clear out the better. I suppose we're supposed to be involved in a winding-up operation, but it's developed into one great flogging bonanza. No, no, you've nothing to worry about. I promise I won't make you sign for anything, and when your time comes to go home you can leave with a clear conscience.'

'What about Captain Crump? Is he in the same boat?'

'He's a very silly girl is Crump. He actually took over the Workshop from his predecessor, actually put his name to a piece of paper.'

'No wonder he looks worried. He lost his last lathe last night.'

'That's about all he would lose. No one would want her virginity, would they?' giggled Geoffrey. 'Now don't worry your head about Crump. Let him stew in his own juice. He's so common anyway. Just to preserve the proprieties you'll forgive me if I act the Major just a tiny bit when he's around.'

'Naturally.'

'I knew you'd understand. Morons like Crump are so apt to get the wrong idea, and we don't want that to happen do we? Now lets finish the champagne and then I'm whisking you into Naples to a rather amusing trattoria I know. Quite an extraordinary boy sings there. Sometimes I think he must be a castrato. I'd so like to hear your professional opinion. Who knows? You might have more success than me and be able to discover the truth. I can promise you he's not an altogether unattractive little goldfish.'

I can remember little of that evening with Major Geoffrey Miller, except that the food was among the best I had ever eaten in Italy. As the night progressed Geoffrey's conversation became more and more outrageous. He was slightly put out when I declined the services of the castrato. It occurred to me before we returned to camp and I finally collapsed on my bed at four in the morning that he might regret his indiscretions later, and a nasty reaction could set in.

Accordingly it was with some trepidation that I reported to the Orderly Room at nine o'clock to discover what duties if any I would have to perform.

Captain Crump was already there, complaining bitterly to Geoffrey about the thieving habits of his guards.

'I can't go on like this, Major,' he was shouting. 'I can't go on. Soon there won't be a spanner left in the place. God knows, what's going to happen when Area finds out what's been going on.'

'Calm down, Captain Crump. May I suggest you go away and write it all down on paper. Then we'll go through it together and I'll forward it on to Higher Authority.' He turned to me. 'I think Captain Nelson you had better spend the day getting the *feel* of the Company. Sergeants Crouch and Wright will fill in the details. If you're in any difficulty I am sure Captain Crump will do everything in his power to help you.'

I thought I detected just the shadow of a wink in Geoffrey Miller's eye.

'You'll do everything to help Captain Nelson, won't you, Captain Crump?' he continued.

Crump mumbled something incomprehensible, saluted, and left the room.

When the door had closed, Geoffrey sighed, 'Such a brute.'

'What's that about Higher Authority?'

'My dear, Crump is so stupid that he thinks I mean what I say. As long as I can keep him writing out reams and reams of reports he's as happy as a sandboy. By the way, why is a sandboy happy, Michael?'

I shook my head.

'Then we'll never know. Off you go then, and have a look round. By the way what Crouch and Wright can't tell you, the old villain Pietro will. I want you on parade in your best frock to go with me to the opera tonight. *Elisir d'Amore*. Slight but amusing. But you must make an effort to look pretty. I'm afraid I can't be seen with you decked out like an old desert rat. All so *vieux jeu*, don't you think? I believe you brought a servant with you. Give him my compliments and tell him he must do better, much better.'

I imparted this information to Driver Tibbs whose only reaction was to raise his eyes.

'Please, Tibbs, do this one last thing for my sake,' I pleaded. 'You have only a few weeks to serve, and this looks like being the cosiest billet it's ever been your good luck to find.'

'If I'm not careful I shall drink myself to death. I've never seen anyone put it back like those two Sergeants. We were at it till six o'clock this morning. You aren't in the same class as them two, Sir. Must say they're a bit of all right. Insisted I join them in their Mess till it's time for me to take my ticket home.'

'Aren't there any other drivers here?'

'No, Sir. I gather the Major, Captain Crump and yourself are the only officers. Then there's Sergeant Wright and Sergeant Crouch and myself, and the rest are all bloody wops. What they're up to fair makes me sick. Funny to think they were our mortal enemies only a couple of years ago, and now they're strutting about as if they own the bloody place.'

'It's their country, Tibbs,' I said.

'As far as I am concerned they can stick it right up. Once I'm home in Blighty nothing will ever get me out of the Old Country again. Had enough travelling in foreign parts to last me a lifetime. As for foreign cunt, Sir, it's not a touch on the homemade stuff. Look at these Eytie bints. All right at fifteen but over the top by eighteen and most of them poxy into the bargain.'

In the company of Driver Tibbs, Sergeant Wright and Sergeant Crouch I made a tour of the camp that morning, and gradually elicited more information about what the company was supposed to be doing. Its main function was to provide transport for the benefit of the local population, carry building material for roads and houses, food in the form of grain and olive oil, and at the same time offer some form of bus service for the local population.

It was a farce. Apart from a purely nominal display of carrying out its function, the whole company was devoted to providing transport for the local black marketeers.

When I expressed my amazement that this was being done so openly and on such a vast scale I received from Driver Tibbs an answer which summed up almost everybody's attitude to these kinds of goings-on after the war in Italy.

'What can we do about it? Make a lot of trouble and end up with a cut throat? What the hell anyway. The whole bloody country's corrupt and rotten to the core and all I want to do is to get home as quickly as possible.'

I was introduced to Pietro, the boss of the whole show, who according to Sergeant Wright was high up in the Salerno Mafia. To look at Pietro one would not imagine that he was capable of any guile let alone any crime.

Pietro was in his early sixties. He carried with him an avuncular aura, never raised his voice, was impeccably polite, and yet everyone of the civilian drivers walked in fear of him.

Taking a lead from my Sergeants I quickly came to an understanding with Pietro. We were discussing the activities of the company over a bottle of the local vino when he laid his hand gently on my shoulder and said: 'Dear Capitano, I can feel that you are *molto sympatico*. So you will make no trouble, will you? I expect you will be going soon, so may I suggest you enjoy your last few months in our country to the full.' He leant forward and filled my glass.

I noticed that he did not refill his own. This did not surprise me, as I had noticed during my wanderings around Italy that the Italians hardly drank at all. I had sometimes wondered what they must have thought of the occupying armies, many of whose members were in a permanent state of drunkenness.

'My dear Pietro, you have nothing to worry about. We have a saying in my country: "What the eye does not see, the heart cannot grieve over".'

'*Capito, capito*,' said Pietro. He found this very funny and put his head back and roared with laughter. 'My dear Capitano, I am so pleased we understand each other. Now if there is anything you need do not hesitate to ask me. Let there be no barriers to impair our friendship. You will find this an expensive town. The *guerra* has done much damage to it and to our finances. So just let me know . . .'

'Pietro, I admire your honesty' I said. 'I have plenty of lire at the moment, but I shall be pleased to call at your Bank should the necessity arise.'

'You speak with great delicacy,' said Pietro. 'You will be like a son to me.'

For the first time his face looked sad. 'Yes, Capitano, you shall be like a son to me. You see I lost my two boys. They were killed when your armies came here to Salerno.'

'I am sorry, Pietro,' I said. 'That's *la guerra*.'

'I detest *la guerra*. You are a young man and no doubt you are interested in the signorinas. Not like the Maggiore, eh? How do you call that, the English vice? Still he is a good man, is the Maggiore and gives us no trouble. He spends the whole time at the opera or looking at the Germans down the road in their short trousers.' Pietro spat on the ground. 'That's what I think of the *tedeschi*. Bastards.'

Not wishing to get involved in a political argument I said, 'Yes, I like the girls.'

'Good. If you want a girl you come to me first. Many of them are diseased. The last Capitano who was here he finished up in the *hospidale* with a dose of the *clapito*. And my dear Captain when our girls give you the *clapito* here you can be sure you got it real and good.'

'In that case I think I'll stick to my other pastime, the bottle.'

'You do that, Capitano. I will have sent up to you and the Maggiore some more of our good wines. Don't buy any of the vino in Salerno. It is all rubbish. How does Sergeant Wright say? All piss.'

We shook hands sealing a friendship that was to last till the day I left that remarkable company.

It did not take me long to discover the principal rackets. The most lucrative was the Olive Oil run from Sicily. There was throughout Italy a chronic shortage of olive oil. During the fighting the olive trees had been neglected, and their harvest neither gathered in nor pressed. The whole basis of Italian cooking rests on olive oil. The cultivation and production of oil was almost back to normal in Sicily which had begun to recover from the devastation of the war as it had been the first to suffer it. Sicily now had a considerable surplus of oil to export. The problem was transport. This was where my civilian company came into its own.

Every day four or five three-ton lorries were sent south to Reggio where they loaded the oil which had been shipped across the narrow straights from Messina. I calculated that during my stay at Salerno there were always some twenty trucks or more somewhere on the road between Salerno and Reggio.

It was difficult for me to assess exactly the amount of money that was being made by the organizers of this racket. According to Sergeant Wright each lorry cleared a profit of something like ten thousand pounds on the trip.

There was a small contingent of Military Police in the area but they presented no problem, being on a percentage with the local criminals. The real problem were the Italian police who were beginning to take over their former role, and demanded excessive cuts. To prevent them tampering with our transport one of my jobs was to patrol the perilous roads between Salerno and Reggio to ensure they did not hold up my trucks and demand unreasonable ransoms.

Never once at the time did I consider my indifference reprehensible. The war was over. I had taken part in it even if I had done nothing to bring it to a successful conclusion. I was extremely anti the Italian people as a whole. I regarded their stab in the back when France fell as unforgivable. Along with the Germans they had caused me to waste the tender years of my life in an atmosphere which I had found utterly uncongenial. Like all part-time soldiers my thoughts were on civvy street and England. That was our Mecca and somehow we felt that when we returned home and were once again civilians some miracle would occur and we would become different people over night. It is easy to sneer today and say that we must have been mad to have entertained such dreams. But we did.

The reason that I did not establish my own personal fortune in Italy is that it simply did not enter my mind. I wasn't made out to be a star criminal. As long as I had sufficient cash in my pocket to live like King Croesus at the time, I was happy. You might say I was not greedy.

Today I very much regret having failed to build up a solid fortune during my last year in Italy, especially when I read of fortunes that are being made daily on the Stock Exchange and by that disgusting post-war breed, the property developers.

Both Sergeant Wright and Sergeant Crouch were wise virgins, though not in the literal sense. I am not sure of the exact details, but I gather they banked about the equivalent of half-a-million pounds each in Italy, returned to England, and waited until the time was ripe when they began to move it over bit by bit.

Sergeant Wright bought a farm in Hampshire and was kind enough to ask me to have a bang at the cocks last year. He is highly thought of in the village, has become a fervent churchgoer, while his wife does the flowers.

Sergeant Crouch unfortunately failed to settle down. He never grew accustomed to his wealth, and took to the bottle in a big way. After several attempts to dry out in the London Clinic he went on a monumental bender and was found dead in his bed having suffocated on his own vomit. At least he left his wife and children well provided for.

The only cloud on the horizon in those days was Captain Crump, who became more and more morose and hostile. He had developed a strong persecution complex which was not alleviated by the friendship which grew up between Major Miller and myself.

'I can't see what you see in the silly sod,' he said to me one day as we were having a drink together before lunch. 'You spend all the time with him at the opera or dining out in Naples. What's the matter with me? Do I smell or something?'

'No, Bill. I like you very much.'

'Then why don't you ask me to go out on the piss with you? God knows you drink enough. What's Major Miller got that I haven't? He's a right funny bugger too. No, it beats me how a sensible chap like you can get mixed up with a looney like him.'

I made one effort to be pleasant to him and we spent an evening together in Naples. It was not a success. I took him to Geoffrey's favourite restaurant and he sent back every course and ended up by stuffing himself with platefuls of eggs and chips. Even these did not come up to his specifications owing to the absence of Daddies sauce. By the time we reached the brothel that had been recommended to me as being reasonably clean by Pietro, he was too far gone to put up much of a performance. I was so bored by the whole evening that Venus herself could not have stirred me from my depression. Leaving Bill to do his best for Britain, I returned to Salerno.

Unfortunately, news of my visit to the brothel reached Geoffrey's ears. He was most displeased, refused to speak to me for three days, and kept asking me whether I had taken the trouble to bathe, since exposing myself to contamination by the ladies of Naples. As a further precaution against any whiff of the female anatomy reaching him, he drenched himself with frequent libations of Chanel No 5.

After I had been forgiven we continued with our nightly visits to Naples going to the opera or dining out in one of its many restaurants, all out of bounds to Allied Troops, but filled with officers and the local black marketeers.

During the intervals at the opera Geoffrey insisted that we promenade together. I shall never forget those evenings as we walked up and down the vast salon arm in arm, while Geoffrey kept up a flow of comment on the local talent.

'Rather pretty, my dear, over there to the left. The one with the dark hair. And what about that cherub? I do fancy her. Shall we ask her to dine with us later?' He would squeeze my arm and giggle.

I think he was disappointed that I showed little interest in the local talent and now and again he would get cross and remark: 'Visiting that disgusting brothel was nothing but a blind. Whom are you trying to fool, Michael?'

The extraordinary thing about Geoffrey was that he did not care how he behaved. To use his own phrase he 'was determined to get himself a ball'.

In the spring of 1946 Geoffrey received news that he was to proceed to England where he would be demobbed. I think he was sad to go, but unlike me he had some kind of family business to return to, connected with the Stock Exchange. Three weeks before his departure he decided to visit Rome and Florence to take a final taste of Italian culture. I suspected that by now he had exhausted most of the local entertainment, and wanted a change.

The day after Geoffrey had driven off in the direction of Rome the trouble started.

The moment I went into Pietro's office I sensed something was wrong. For the first time he looked agitated.

'Signor Capitano, something dreadful has happened,' he said wringing his hands. 'I have to tell you, Capitano, that there are dishonest men in our midst. Worse, Capitano, there are thieves among my men. I trusted each one of them and now two of them steal from me. I would not have believed it possible. Men that I trusted like my own brothers.'

After lamenting the lack of honesty among his drivers I gathered that two of them had made off with their lorries to the north, after returning fully loaded with olive oil from the south. On reaching Milan they had disposed of the oil for a vast sum. Not satisfied with that they had sold both of the trucks for an even greater sum, thereby ensuring themselves a comfortable old age.

'Surely your organization will not permit this?' I said. By now I had a fair idea of the strength of the local Mafia. 'When they come back, they will have a lot to answer for?'

It transpired that they had already returned to their native village of Vietri just north of Salerno. Here they had placed themselves under the protection of the local carabinieri whose chief was also the brother of one of them. It also appeared that both men were connected by marriage to most of the families in the village, who would do everything in their power to oppose their extradition.

My reaction was one of extreme irritation. I did not care a damn about the loss of the olive oil, but I was annoyed by the casual selling of W.D. Transport. The loss of two three-tonners might seem a small matter, but it might be difficult to explain away. Although it was unlikely that it would reach the ears of high authority, there was always the chance. One thing I did not want was to be detained longer than necessary in Italy, least of all by a Court of Enquiry as to how two trucks from a R.A.S.C. civilian Transport Company in Salerno came to be sold in the markets of Milan. Nor was I oblivious of the danger that once this crime had come to light, further examples of the misuse of the army's transport might be exposed to the glare of publicity.

I did not hesitate. I summoned Sergeants Wright and Crouch and Driver Tibbs, ordered them to arm themselves with sub-machine guns and several magazines, and to pick me and Pietro up at once in a fifteen-hundredweight truck.

As we roared off in the direction of Vietri with Driver Tibbs at the wheel, I offered up a prayer that all would be well, that what I was doing was the right thing. It would be tragedy if, after all the vicissitudes which I had overcome, I should end up a fatal casualty in the streets of the one-cob village of Vietri.

Putting myself in Montgomery's shoes I calculated that my advantage was the element of surprise. The enemy would be unprepared for so sudden a reaction on my part, and with luck I could be in amongst them and out again with my prisoners before they knew what had hit them. To use the General's phrase, I intended to knock them for six.

Without slackening speed we reached Vietri in fifteen minutes, scattering chickens, women and children and the usual collection of loafing Italian men in all directions. With a screech of brakes we slid to a halt in front of the local police station. We were inside and the door locked behind us, our guns at the ready in a matter of seconds. Within a minute Sergeants Crouch and Wright had the local chief of police over the table beating the daylight out of him and threatening to execute him on the spot if he did not hand over the two offenders without further ado.

I noticed that Pietro was delighted with the punishment that the two Sergeants were handing out, and was visibly disappointed when the victim screamed for mercy and promised to hand over the miscreants.

A terrified carabiniere was dispatched to summon the two men to the police station with orders that on no account was he to tell them what they were wanted for.

Five minutes later they walked into our trap. Before they could protest, let alone put up any show of resistance, we had bundled them into the truck at gun point, and were scorching our way out of the village.

In spite of repeated requests by Pietro that they should be handed over to him, I insisted on driving them into Naples where I handed them over to the Neapolitan police, ordering that they should be charged with stealing army property. To ensure that this happened I called in on the local Assistant Provost Marshal, informed him of my action and was warmly congratulated on my swift and successful arrests.

In spite of his disappointment, Pietro appreciated that I had saved him a great deal of bother and his face at the same time.

'You acted like a true son of mine, Capitano,' he told me. 'Now every man of mine will respect you and will not get up to such dirty and dishonourable thieving.'

When troubles come they certainly come not singly but in battalions. I was sitting in the Mess before lunch listening to Bill Crump's unending tales of woe when Sergeant Wright knocked at the door and came in bearing a buff envelope marked *Most Secret*.

'Bad news, Sir,' he said handing it to me. 'I took the liberty of looking at it, as I did not feel you would wish your meal to be disturbed unnecessarily.'

It was very bad news. In its wisdom H.Q. Naples had decided that all our civilian drivers should be dismissed within the next seven days. To make matters worse their place would be taken by German prisoners-of-war.

It looked sensible on paper. What was the point of having thousands of P.O.W.'s about the place eating their heads off and doing nothing, while paying Italian civilians to drive trucks? Anyway, that's the way I figured out Headquarters had reasoned. Unfortunately they had not considered the implications of their order.

'Do the Italian drivers know about this?'

'Of course, Sir,' said Sergeant Wright, 'There's no such thing as security any longer now that they employ all those Eytie bints in the offices at H.Q. There's pretty near a riot already taking place in the waggon lines.'

'This looks like your kettle of fish, Bill,' I said.

Bill shook his head. 'No you don't, old boy. I'm strictly a workshops man. You're the admin wallah, old chap.'

I went to the telephone and got through to Headquarters in Naples, only to be told by an impertinent girl on the switchboard that everyone was at lunch and were not expected back until after siesta around about four o'clock.

When I finally managed to contact a staff Captain I was rudely received.

'Look here, old man, you've just received an order. Kindly carry it out and don't worry us here with ill-disciplined complaints. We're terribly under-staffed here and have more important matters to deal with.'

'You understand that this could mean a riot?'

'Don't talk such rubbish, old boy. In any case you've got some soldiers with you, haven't you?'

'Two sergeants and a driver. Couldn't you send me a company of infantry to keep the peace?'

'Are you out of your mind? What did you say your name was? Nelson? Listen, Nelson, kindly carry out your orders or I shall be compelled to put in a report of your incompetence to the Brigadier.'

The telephone went dead.

With a weary heart I went to find Pietro to appeal to his better nature and try to get him to prevent his men from opposing the German P.O.W.'s when they arrived to take over the lorries.

Pietro would not listen to me.

'If I could control my men, which I cannot, I would still not help you, Capitano, although you are my son and a brave soldier. It was the *tedeschi* that ruined my country and brought us so much suffering. They kill my sons, and now they come again to take the bread out of our children's mouths.'

For the first time I lost my temper with Pietro. 'Listen, you old villain,' I shouted. 'Don't give me all that sentimental shit. You're all one bloody great band of robbers, and well you know it. All right, go ahead and try to fight the teds, and see what happens to you. They'll knock the hell out of you and I shan't do a thing to protect you.'

'I shall destroy all the lorries first rather than hand them over to the *tedeschi*.'

I knew he was speaking the truth.

That evening I held a conference with Sergeants Wright and Crouch and Driver Tibbs.

Our determination not to get involved in a war between the Germans and the Italians was unanimous. At the same time I was slightly apprehensive of what Headquarters might do to me if they discovered that some sixty army trucks had gone up in flames, while I stood to one side and did nothing to try to prevent it. Accordingly I ordered my two sergeants together with Driver Tibbs to arm themselves to the hilt, and whatever they might feel within, to adopt an appearance of aggression without.

That evening when most of the Italian drivers had returned to the camp, we made a visit to the lines.

I did not like the atmosphere one little bit. On all sides we were surrounded by angry men gesticulating and shouting at us.

When Pietro had managed to quieten the mob I addressed them as follows:

'I know exactly how you feel. But you must understand that I have my orders and as a soldier I must obey them, whatever the cost. I have been commanded by those in authority to disband this company and hand over its trucks to the *tedeschi*.'

Ignoring the shouts and the boos I continued. 'I would have thought that everyone of you had had enough of the *guerra*. All I can say to you is that if you oppose my orders the *guerra* will come to you again. I have spoken with my General and he has promised me strong support. If you do not obey me men will come with armoured cars and tanks to see that his orders are carried out. Is this what you want? Do you wish to see more bloodshed and death in the streets of Salerno? Because this is what you will see if you do not do as you are told.'

The crowd was silent.

Following up my advantage I continued: 'I promise you one thing. I will do all in my power to see that this order is withdrawn. Personally I think it is a mistake. Like you I do not wish to command the *tedeschi* who are still my enemies and against whom I have fought for four long years. Now go back to your homes and stop this silly talk of war.'

Driver Tibbs said: 'Bloody marvellous, Captain. Didn't know you had it in you. What's all this talk of armoured cars and tanks? Thought you told us earlier that we could expect no support.'

'Nor can we, driver. We are the tanks and the armoured cars. We stand alone.'

'Not me. Not bloody likely. I'm for civvy street and a load of bloody wops aren't going to see me lay down my life to make theirs safe for robbery.'

I spent an anxious night. Looking at the problem from all angles I could find no way to resolve it. If the Germans came there would be trouble. Of that I was sure. The hatred between them and the Italians was so intense that I did not doubt for one moment that the Italians would initially try to resist the takeover. In the process some of them would get killed before they capitulated and turned tail as they surely would.

I was saved by a telephone call. It was the same staff Captain at Headquarters Naples on the other end of the line.

'Yesterday's orders are cancelled. Confirmation is on its way by D.R.'

'What made you change your mind?' I asked.

'Lots of lily-livered idiots like you all over the area are saying they can't control a handful of Eytie civilians and demanding protection which we haven't got.'

Before I could tell him to get stuffed he slammed down his telephone.

I reported the news to my Sergeants and Driver Tibbs who were extremely relieved. I told Pietro that it was my diplomatic manner with Headquarters which had averted the catastrophe.

For a moment I thought he was going to burst into tears. He put his arms around me. 'Not only are you a man of action, you are a man of infinite wisdom,' he said. 'I beg of you, my Capitano, to stay with me here in Salerno and be my son. There would be no limit to your future here. You would be a very great man.'

Next day I was ordered to report to Naples to take command of a transport company manned entirely by Germans.

Chapter Nine

The following morning I said good-bye to Bill Crump, who regarded my posting as a personal insult. He was to take over command of the company in the absence of Major Geoffrey Miller, which he did under protest, affirming that he was a mechanical and not a administrative wallah. He refused to sign for a single piece of equipment, which did not worry me, as I had not done so either.

I bade farewell to Driver Tibbs who had not been posted with me. I did make a tentative enquiry as to whether he would care to join me if I could pull the right string. He declined the offer. I suspect that he was beginning to work some profitable racket. Like Driver Lane, after we had severed our successful partnership, we never met again.

At 1000 hrs the following morning I drank a farewell bottle of the finest Chianti with Sergeants Wright and Crouch and Pietro, who was in tears at the prospect of my departure and was still urging me not to behave too stupidly but to throw in my lot with him and remain in Salerno. He could not understand that I was still subject to military discipline. In the end he gave up and went into a sulk, though not before promising me that he would speak to members of his family in Naples who would get in touch with me, take me to their bosoms and see that I lacked nothing.

At 1030 hrs Driver Tibbs came into the Mess where we were about to broach a second bottle, and announced that a staff car with a Ted at the wheel had arrived from Naples to pick me up.

This was my first real contact with the enemy. Accordingly I intimated to both sergeants that they would be doing me a favour if they came outside to see me on my way.

In the drive before the villa stood an immaculate staff car. It shone to high heaven. I could see that someone had been hard at work with paraffin. A German with stripes on his arms was busy removing specks of dirt from its bonnet. Hearing us come out of the villa and walk towards him, he sprang to attention, threw me up an immaculate salute and remained standing to attention.

I could see that Driver Tibbs was shocked. 'Bull-shitting lot of bastards,' he said.

I noticed the clean K.D. that the German Corporal was wearing, not a crease out of place.

'Let that be an example to you how a soldier should be turned out, Driver Tibbs,' I said.

'So what?' said Driver Tibbs. 'Fat lot of bloody good it did them. We won the fucking war, didn't we?'

I shook hands with everyone.

'Thank you for all you've done to make my stay here a happy one,' I said.

This expression of tenderness occasioned a further flood of tears on Pietro's part. Before I could avoid him he had thrown his arms round my neck and was kissing me on both cheeks.

The two Sergeants threw me salutes. Driver Tibbs contented himself with saying, 'Cheerio, Captain Nelson. Take care of the crumpet in Napoli. It's pretty poxy from all reports.' Pietro continued to weep aloud, his shoulders shaking with emotion.

I walked towards the staff car. The Corporal saluted me a second time, stepped forward smartly, and opened the rear door to allow me to enter. Closing it behind me, he walked in a soldierly manner to the front, got in, sat bolt upright, but made no further move.

It struck me that I was in a ridiculous position, sitting in the back of a stationary staff car.

It was not until the German Corporal said: 'Permission to go, Herr Hauptmann?' that I realized that I was now commanding a highly disciplined company of soldiers who expected to receive orders which they would obey without hesitation. Accordingly I said: 'Forward, Corporal.'

This had the desired effect, and as I raised my hand and waved at my Sergeants, Driver Tibbs and Pietro, he let in the clutch and we moved forward so gently that I felt like the King of England on an inspection of his troops.

The company which I was to take over was stationed in a former Italian Army barracks in the northern suburbs of Naples.

As we drove through its imposing gates I saw at once that this would be nothing like the Italian barracks at Bari in which it had been my misfortune to suffer earlier in the year.

On all sides, as we crossed the square, I could sense a military atmosphere. From extreme distances German soldiers turned their eyes and heads sharply in the direction of my car and threw me magnificent salutes, which I returned timidly, once again feeling that I was the centre of a royal procession.

Everywhere, I could see the signs of discipline. Fire buckets were ranged along the walls of the buildings; whitened ropes coiled around like snakes; on the far side of the square what must have been a punishment squad was crawling across the square gathering twigs and dust as they went, under the eyes of a brute of a German warrant-officer; here and there patches of flowers bloomed in well-kept beds.

My Corporal drew the car to a halt in front of what must have been the Orderly Room. Somewhat incongruously, above it a flag bearing the colours of the R.A.S.C. drooped in the windless air.

Before I could let myself out of the car the Corporal had hurried round, swung open the door and saluted me as I dismounted.

Suddenly on all sides the air was rent by the shouts of guttural voices. For a moment I was tempted to turn tail and flee.

From the Guard Room stampeded some twenty Germans, all beautifully turned out in K.D., carrying pick helms at the slope in place of rifles.

With the skill of Guardsmen they formed up in front of the Orderly Room under the command of a German Major. The next moment he had bellowed an order, and with a precision that I have never seen before, they were giving me a Present Arms. This was the first time I had been accorded this honour, due only to those with the rank of Major and above. The Major in command came forward, saluted me, and said in perfect English,

'Guard ready for your inspection, Herr Hauptmann.'

I must admit as I walked along the lines of those magnificently turned-out soldiers, I was only too conscious of what a shabby figure I must have cut, with my ill-fitting, vino-stained uniform. At least the men on parade were not aware of how much fear they inspired in me.

When the inspection was over, the Major conducted me to my living quarters. These were magnificent, if simply furnished, with matting on the floor, a proper bed, a dining table with four chairs, and two armchairs. In one corner was an imposing cocktail cabinet.

Seeing me eyeing it the Major opened it and said, 'I think, Sir, you will find here all you need.'

This was the first time I have ever been called 'Sir' by a Major. For a moment I thought of correcting him, but decided that it would only embarrass him. I was, after all, on the victorious side and entitled to respect from the vanquished. For the remainder of my stay, I continued to permit him to address me so.

'Your luncheon will be served in half-an-hour, Sir.'

'Where do I mess?'

'Here, Sir.'

'On my own?'

The Major looked surprised. 'But yes, Sir. The last Captain messed here on his own.'

'What do you and your officers do?'

He looked even more surprised. 'We have our own mess, Sir.'

I could see that he had no intention of asking me to join him, so I assumed that this was the protocol that I would have to follow, although I did not look forward with any joy to eating and drinking on my own.

Immediately after the war there was a ridiculous order about non-fraternization with our ex-enemies, which included the women as well. It was a failure from the start. Having won the war the one thing the victorious soldier was interested in were women, whom he rightly regarded as the spoils of war.

It was with a heavy heart that I ate my solitary meal which was served by the corporal who had picked me up in the staff car. I was increasingly saddened as he waited on me at the table and insisted on jumping to attention every time I asked for something. It is extremely disconcerting when even a simple request such as asking for the salt produces an automaton's reaction.

It was about two o'clock when I ventured out onto the square. I saw at once that there was no siesta as far as the Germans were concerned. The punishment squad was still busy licking the tarmac clean; rows of lorries, which must have come in while I was eating my lunch, were drawn up in straight lines and being washed down and wiped dry; now and again the odd squad would swing past me and give me a sharp eyes right. Over the whole place was a military atmosphere such as I had not encountered since I had been inducted into the Corps as a driver nearly five years before. It made me feel depressed.

Having decided to discover what went on, what the purpose of the company was, and if there were any other British on the establishment apart from myself, I sauntered into the Orderly Room.

Stupidly I had let my guard down and lulled myself into a sense of false security.

Before the door had closed behind me there was a series of guttural roars and once again pandemonium broke loose, as everyone including the Major sprang to attention behind their desks.

Forgetting myself I spoke the first words that came into my head. 'Carry on Sergeant.'

No sooner had I said this than I saw a look of sorrow cross the face of the German Major. Not a man moved, and it was not until I had said:

'Please carry on with whatever you're doing, Major,' that he barked out some incomprehensible command and everyone returned to their papers and pencils.

I noticed that the walls were covered with graphs, strengths, numbers of lorries, numbers of men sick or about to go sick, defaulters and everything else that a commanding officer might care to have at his finger tips.

Frankly it frightened me. Not for the last time during the months that I was to command that company of Germans I asked myself how in the devil had they managed to lose the war?

The Major conducted me into the inner office and stood before me. It was not until I indicated that he should take the weight off his legs that he reluctantly acceded to my request.

The first piece of information that I elicited was that there was only one British Corporal, formerly of the London Scottish, attached to the company. The Major seemed vague about his whereabouts, but I gathered that he showed up for morning and evening parades.

The Major was very keen on parades and held them at every opportunity, being of the opinion that parades instilled into the men under his command the constant reminder that they were still soldiers in the German Army which, although it may have been defeated, was not a rabble like the Italian Army.

The men under his command came from all units of the German Army. There were engineers, infanteers, gunners, cavalrymen and even a few members of the Luftwaffe.

The function of the company was twofold. First of all it collected rations from the port, brought them to an area in the camp where they were divided, and from there they were delivered to the surrounding P.O.W. camps, or to units of the German Army outside the wire who were being employed on the numerous reconstruction projects. These included road-making, bridge building and work on the land.

Although the war was over for the German soldiers who drove the lorries, a second war had constantly to be waged against their former allies. Quite a number of the latter operated in highly-organized gangs and were constantly attempting to hijack lorry-loads of food for profitable disposal on the black market. There was no question of any of it going to the poor of Naples who were on the verge of starvation. It was flogged to the rich and the proceeds of the sales went directly into the pockets of the gangs.

As a result no lorry ever left camp without at least two men in the cab and two in the back. Those in the rear were armed with picks or iron bars with which to repel attacks. They were bitter because they were not permitted to carry firearms which put them at a considerable disadvantage since many of the gangs were armed to the teeth with tommy guns, pistols and even machine guns.

The second function of the conpany was the disposal of ammunition of all shapes and sizes. A considerable amount was still being shipped into the port of Naples although the war had been over nearly a year. Much of it came from North Africa, and some from the U.K. It was as if no one could stop this ceaseless flow, which was no longer required. I assumed that it was in the pipeline and would continue to arrive until the pipe ran dry.

During that summer in Naples I saw and handled more ammunition than I had done throughout the whole war. When I say I handled, I mean of course that the Germans humped the stuff. Sometimes I thought I was living in Wonderland, and at times I was anxious for my sanity.

I would be informed that a Liberty ship had docked in the port with a cargo of ammo. Landing sheet after landing sheet would be delivered to my office detailing, down to the last two-inch mortar-bomb and round of 303 ammunition, the exact nature and quantity of the shipment. These lists I handed over to the German Major, who made no comment whatever he might have thought.

Within a few hours trucks would be dispatched to the docks and the unloading of the shipment would get under way.

It was obviously not practical or even in the interests of safety to dump the stuff in or near our camp. Accordingly dumps were set up in the hills around the city, and here were unloaded millions of pounds of assorted ammunition. It was all neatly stacked and labelled. I could walk for miles through the olive groves, counting thousands of rounds of twenty-five pounders, millions of boxes of 303, all neatly labelled and stowed away.

There were no military guards on these dumps and they provided a natural source of plunder for the local bandits.

When the Liberty ship had been unloaded and departed, no doubt to bring in further supplies to this war zone, where a war no longer existed, the second part of the operation commenced.

My lorries would be dispatched to the dumps to reload the stuff. It was carefully checked onto the trucks and all shortages caused by raiders and others in search of gunpowder were duly noted down on sheets of paper. From the dumps it was driven to the small port of Castellammare some thirty miles south of Naples. Here it was checked and loaded onto Landing Craft.

From the port of Castellammare the landing craft sailed forth. At a spot decided on by Higher Authority it was dumped overboard.

I found the procedure bizarre. The Germans went about it with ruthless efficiency. The losses caused by the bandits' raids on the dumps resulting in serious discrepancies between what came off the Liberty ships in Naples and what was thrown back into the sea off Castellammare, caused them endless nights of lost sleep.

When there were no Liberty ships to unload, I found myself riding south with convoys to locate dumps of ammunition that had been established in some cases as long ago as two years. Many of them were in a state of neglect and in a dangerous condition. Although these latter in no way intimidated the German sappers who were attached to the company, they scared the pants off me. Accordingly any dump that they reported to be in the slightest way dicey, I took care to pass by on the other side.

During the summer of 1946 I must have located more rounds of ammunition of all makes and sizes than was loosed off in the entire Italian campaign. I think that if I had been a gunner I would have gone raving made and shot myself remembering the limitations that were placed on the number of rounds per gun that might be fired daily because of the perpetual shortage of ammunition at the sharp end.

The nearer the sharp end the greater the shortage, was a favourite maxim, but it did not apply only to ammunition. I cannot remember servicing a single brigade—and owing to my constant postings due to the determination of a host of sensible commanding officers to dispense with my services, I serviced a great number—which was not short of everything it needed. It didn't matter if it were battle-dresses, shells, boots, bombs, French letters, transport, guns, or toothbrushes, you could guarantee that there would be a shortage once you got down to Brigade level. As you walked away from the front their supply increased rapidly. At Division the supply position could be described as fair; at Corps good; at Army very good; and at the ports of supply excellent to bloody magnificent.

The reason for this state of affairs was entirely due to the 'Umbrella'.

No officer in charge of any kind of dump liked to find himself short. Accordingly, by never-ceasing rounds of fiddles, he built up considerable hidden reserves.

The port supply officer would tell the fellow from the Army: 'Can let you have twenty thousand shirts, old boy, and I don't mind telling you that I'm doing you a favour', while at the same time retaining the other twenty thousand in a warehouse near the docks, where they would be gradually whittled away by the local thieves.

The Army wallah would say to his opposite number at Corps: 'Can let you have ten thousand shirts, old chap.' He in turn would store the other ten thousand in a local barn where they would nourish the rats and mice.

The fellow from Corps would go forward to Division and hear the guns and promise delivery of five thousand shirts. The wretched fellow at Division who was always being bollocked by his General for failing to give the men the tools with which to finish the job, usually suffered from ulcers. But he was determined not to be caught out again, so off he goes to Brigade at which level the actual fighting is done, and promises a delighted Brigade Commander some two thousand shirts, slightly less than one for two men. In fact the situation is worse than this. An infantry brigade consists of five thousand men, only half of whom will be right up at the sharp end. By the time the shirts have been handled by various quartermasters each of whom will put up an umbrella in turn, one shirt for every four fighting men would finally arrive from the consignment of forty thousand originally landed.

No wonder Churchill kept growling through his cigars about the vast number of men deployed throughout the world, of whom only the minutest fraction ever acutally fought the enemy. Churchill was a great man and a great war leader, but this was his biggest failure. In spite of threats of public hangings, he never succeeded in changing the shape of the forces. He would like to have seen them ranged against the enemy in the shape of an inverted pyramid. I suspect the opposition to this reasonable proposition must have emanated at the highest level. I am accusing no one of cowardice. How could I ? How dare I ? I think rather it was a way of thinking that placed an excessive importance on logistics. On the other hand I have not the slightest doubts that there were a great number of temporary soldiers like myself who lived in constant fear of the old warrior getting his way and managing to turn the pyramid upside-down.

As soon as I realized that the Company would not benefit from interference on my part I decided to leave it well alone. I had learned from trying to play around with mechanical transport that was already roadworthy that only disaster could result. I am continually amazed to this day to see thousands of men on a Sunday afternoon messing about with their cars instead of leaving them well alone and carrying out their Sabbath duty which is to pay attention to their wives or girl friends, preferably between the sheets. I can assure them that if their cars break down on Monday as they go to work they have only themselves to blame.

The day after I had taken over the Company I made the acquaintance of Corporal Robertson of the London Scottish. He reported to my billet shortly after I had breakfasted, wearing a kilt. He was anxious to see how I proposed to run the organization. As soon as I had informed him that it was my intention to leave well alone and devote my life to pleasure until such time as His Majesty should no longer require my services, he relaxed. When I told him to help himself to the Scotch on the table, his joy knew no bounds.

It appeared that Corporal Robertson was one of the happy casualties of the war. I never discovered if he was telling the truth, but he swore to me that as far as his battalion was concerned he had been killed during the fighting in Italy. He was not sure of the exact location, nor did he care. The fact was that he had long since been struck off the battalion strength. This suited him admirably, as he detested his wife more than anybody else on earth, and when he finally decided to return to Scotland he intended to find himself a bride and settle down in the Highlands on a croft without running the risk of being charged with bigamy. As he rightly remarked a dead man cannot have two wives at the same time.

Corporal Robertson swore that he was not a deserter. I believed him. His story was too fantastic to be anything but the truth.

He had been sent back to his Field Ambulance during the fighting, suffering from battle exhaustion. Feeling thirsty and being denied any sort of alcohol which he regarded as a greater necessity than water, he had walked out of the place. A very heavy battle was going on at the time and casualties were pouring into the station. In the confusion, which was not helped by the Germans putting down a heavy barrage and killing a number of personnel including two of the doctors, Corporal Robertson's absence was not noticed.

After the battle it was assumed that Corporal Robertson had been killed on the way down to the Field Ambulance, giving his life for his King and Country.

Finally Corporal Robertson, who claimed that he was suffering from loss of memory, turned up at a transit camp outside Naples. Here he had managed to find an A.B. 64 belonging to a Corporal of similar name, although I did not believe this part of his story when he used the word 'find'. From then on it was plain sailing. A few weeks before my arrival the Adjutant of the camp had been asked to supply one Corporal to keep an eye on the German Company and had found Corporal Robertson only too pleased to accept the posting.

The other remarkable thing about Corporal Robertson was that in spite of the extreme heat of the Neapolitan summer he insisted on wearing the kilt, protesting like so many of his race that it was the warmest thing to wear in winter and the coolest in summer. He did, however, have the honesty to confess that the women of Naples were fascinated by it, and were continually putting their hands up to verify his sex.

Soon after we had reached half-way-down the bottle of Scotch Corporal Robertson and I found ourselves in complete agreement, except over one small matter, the slovenliness of my dress.

I had to admit that as far as Corporal Robertson was concerned he looked every inch a soldier. I could not have faulted him on a single point.

'I dinna like you letting Scotland down in front of the enemy, Sirr,' he confided in me. 'If you dinna mind I'll hae the camp tailor tae a look at you. He'll make you a pair o' breeches at the same time.'

When I protested that I did not require breeches he informed me that the German cavalry P.O.W. officers had amassed a fine stables in the lines, and it was the custom to inspect the troops on parade mounted and spurred.

I thanked God that I had learnt to ride on some thoroughly non-thoroughbreds on a farm in Devonshire before the war.

Shortly before lunch that day the German tailor reported to my quarters, measured me up and down, forwards and backwards, and within forty-eight hours delivered two sets of K.D. and two pairs of cavalry breeches the like of which I had never seen before or since.

They fitted me impeccably and as I marched about the camp I felt like Field-Marshal Alexander himself. I was angry with myself for not realizing earlier in my military career how important clothes are. They would have made a two-pipper like myself feel twenty feet tall, and I had not the slightest doubt must have inspired confidence in me on the part of my superiors. Naturally I blamed Driver Lane for having allowed me to go about like a scarecrow with my uniform always in a perpetual state of filth and disarray.

A few days later, mounted on a chestnut charger, I took my first morning parade escorted on either side by two straightbacked cavalry-men of the German Army. I wondered if they were Uhlans. I was glad that they did not carry lances. My only sorrow was that Major Hawkins, in fact all those past commanding officers who had so clearly failed to see any good in me, were not on the touchline to watch me at my finest hour. I hope the Germans were impressed by my upright posture and fine seat. They had no idea of the agony that I suffered during the first week. Every bone in my body cried out for mercy. I had taken no exercise for several years, and they were entitled to complain. But having defeated the Hun on the field of battle I was determined not to be out-done.

One morning in June of that year, I was sitting in my quarters after the morning parade when the German Major knocked at my door, came in, saluted, and said, 'Permission to speak, Herr Hauptmann.'

I nodded wearily, having by now become bored by this perpetual obsequiousness. After weeks of it, I had come to the conclusion that it was because of it that the Germans had lost the war. They seemed to lack initiative. They would only move after orders had been given from above.

'There are three Italians who are asking to see you, Herr Hauptmann. Naturally I have not admitted the swine into the camp. They are still hanging about the camp entrance. Shall I give the guard orders to beat them up?'

'What do they want?'

'They are demanding to see you, Herr Hauptmann. They say they have been sent by Pietro from Salerno.'

'Show them in.'

Not a muscle on the Major's face moved to indicate his annoyance at my intention to receive three Wops. Instead, he saluted, spun about, and left my hut.

A few minutes later he returned with them.

For a minute I thought that I was in the cinema in the days before the war watching a gangster film. In came three dark-skinned Italians wearing identical clothes. The turn-ups on their trousers must have been nearly a foot across; the lapels were nearly six inches wide on the double breasted suits; their ties about the same width. Each one held in his hand a wide-brimmed trilby whose front brim was turned down.

They looked at the German Major without saying a word.

'Thank you, Major,' I said.

'Let me know when you wish them conducted from the camp, Herr Hauptmann,' he replied. From the way he said 'them' I knew he considered them no gentlemen.

As soon as he had saluted and departed the men approached me.

Each one in turn put his arm round my shoulder, kissed me on both cheeks and said, 'Welcome to Naples, Capitano.'

When we were all comfortably seated, and I had placed a bottle of Strega on the table, to which they helped themselves most modestly, their leader, who went by the name of Antonio, said. 'We have heard from our brothers in Salerno of your great kindness, bravery and diplomacy, Capitano. Accordingly we thought it would be in both our interests to make your acquaintance.'

I nodded, not at this point wishing to commit myself in any way.

'We understand from our brothers that you have always been most concerned and amicably disposed towards their good works,' continued Antonio. 'They have suggested to us that you may well out of the kindness of your heart be interested in helping us in the reconstruction in which we are involved.'

'Could be,' I said. 'But you must know one thing. I have not many months to remain here. I would not wish to get involved in any of your philanthropic works which might bring me in conflict with the Military.'

Antonio held up his hands and looked shocked. 'We understand, Capitano. All we have in mind is that you should be happy and enjoy your stay in our beautiful city. We would not wish to cause you any trouble. We will only call upon you for help should our reconstructions run into difficulties that we cannot resolve without you.'

After a further exchange of double talk and pleasantries, in which I was informed that I would always be welcome and looked after at a club off the Via Roma, and all the best restaurants in Naples, the three gentlemen rose to take their leave.

When they reached the door Antonio turned to me and said, 'One last word, Capitano. You may have heard of some evil men in our midst who are operating in bands and ravishing the countryside, and holding up peace-loving citizens. You must take great care not to travel on your own outside of the city. Some of them of course have been informed of your bravery by our brothers at Salerno and, if they recognize you, will not molest you. However there are many deserters of other nations who are ill-disciplined and bringing disgrace upon our country, and these we cannot answer for.'

I was already well-informed about these bands who were operating outside the city holding up army transport. It was true that some were made up of allied deserters, but the majority of them were controlled by the Italians. Since my arrival in Naples I had never gone outside the city on one of my inspections of the ammunition dumps without taking at least three Germans with me, all of whom I issued with Sten guns. I had lost some of my fear of the Hun, and reckoned that it was better to take a chance and issue them with weapons rather than to perish on an Italian mountain road at the hands of a marauding band of deserters.

When I was on my own, the German Major having summoned one of the guards to escort my three visitors off the premises, I pondered the meaning of their visit. It seemed to me that they had something in mind for me. It was obviously crooked and on a big scale. The fact that they would not call upon me except in an emergency was significant. Clearly they were observing tight security and considered the fewer in the know the better. But whereas I did not mind indulging in modest fiddling to enable me to live in the style to which I had grown accustomed, I made up my mind that on no account would I get involved in anything criminal as a result of which I might end up behind bars. I had only a few months to go. I would keep my nose clean.

That afternoon I paid my first visit to the club off the Via Roma. No sooner had I arrived than I was greeted by the head waiter and ushered to a discreet box at the back of the room. I suppose the place held about two hundred people, and it was crowded with rich Italians with their wives or girl friends and a sprinkling of officers although I had noticed an Off Limits sign above its entrance.

Soon after I had settled myself in the box and ordered a bottle of champagne and a dozen oysters, a dark haired Italian girl came onto the small stage and sang selections from opera requested by members of the audience. She sang beautifully and received considerable applause.

Soon after she left the stage I heard the door of the box open and the next moment a girl sat down beside me, and took me by the hand. I could see in the half darkness that it was the girl who had just finished singing.

Squeezing my hand she said, 'Hullo, Capitano. I am Maria. I hope you are well, Capitano.'

We spent the afternoon getting better acquainted, and although she never mentioned anything, it was clear to me that she had been instructed by my visitors of the morning to entertain me. Now and again she had to leave me to return to the stage. By nine o'clock in the evening I was extremely drunk and anxious to take her to bed. As the hours had passed so had her beauty increased. Not that she wasn't beautiful, she was. Her only draw-back as far as I was concerned was that she was extremely small. But her complexion was out of this world and she could not have been more than eighteen years old.

I am sure she was not trying to string me along, but she kept telling me that her last appearance on stage was at ten, and she could not leave before then. I say string along because visitors to night clubs will be familiar with this old gimmick. Artistes, hostesses, or just straight whores will give you this line about not being allowed to leave by the management, while they chalk up drink after drink, or rather coloured water after coloured water at your expense. Then about four in the morning when you are blind with drink they give you the slip, and you come

163

out into the street to find yourself utterly alone with your wallet empty.

I knew she was telling the truth when she came off the stage at ten thirty and returned to my box. I called for the bill. The head waiter informed me that it had been taken care of by my friends.

I can remember Maria helping me into a taxi, and then climbing an endless flight of stairs. The next thing was that I could feel something wet and soft being applied to my aching forehead. I opened my eyes and saw that it was Maria dabbing my face with a sponge.

I was lying in a double bed. The clock on the bedside table said ten. Through my alcoholic haze I wondered who had taken the morning parade at the camp.

After Maria had run me a bath, and I had soaked myself in the hot water and shaved myself with a razor she supplied, I breakfasted with her.

After breakfast she led me back to the bed where we made love.

At one o'clock we went out to a restaurant and had lunch, after which I would have liked to have gone back to her flat. Unfortunately it was not possible because she had to report to the club on the dot of three. I saw that she walked in fear of her bosses and was terrified of being so much as a minute late.

So I fell into this daily routine, although on every third day I insisted that she call me at five, so that I could get back to the camp to take the parade. Never once did the German Major ask me where I had been.

I became very attached to Maria. She was the first slave I had ever possessed, and I can see that slavery has its points. On the other hand I was ashamed of my conduct at the time, knowing that I was using her. Today I bitterly regret the way I behaved, and I am quite sure that if there is a Hell, when I arrive there, this is one of my mortal crimes which will take a great deal of time to expiate. To make matters worse the volume of my drinking increased. From three in the afternoon until half past ten I would sit in the semi-darkness in the box and get completely stoned.

Looking back I can see that Maria felt sorry for me. As she wiped my sweating brow she would croon tender words and keep murmuring, '*Poveretto, poveretto.*' I am sure that not for one moment did she begin to love me; it was rather as if I were some domestic animal in pain which could not help itself, and she could not bear to see it suffer.

This may sound like a bad case of self-pity. But I did not feel sorry for myself. It was merely a continuation of that sense of insecurity that had overtaken me a few months before at Bari, allied to a feeling of utter frustration at being kept in the army.

A month after my arrival in Naples I had had no further communication from the three Italian gentlemen. I was kept aware of their existence as my bill was always paid by someone at the club, and other restaurants, and I naturally assumed they were picking up the tabs.

It must have been early in July, 1946, that I was lunching on my own in a restaurant called the Falstaff. I cannot remember why Maria was not with me. It was not because we had fallen out since during the two months that she looked after me we never had a cross word. Possibly she had gone to the hairdresser; she may have taken the morning off to see her parents who lived down the coast near Amalfi. Anyway, during lunch I became aware of a Captain in army uniform, who was dining with a beautiful blonde at the next table, because he kept glancing at me and whispering to his companion.

I had just asked the waiter to put a bottle of brandy on the table from which I intended to obtain an afternoon's oblivion, when he got up from his chair and stood over me.

'Michael Nelson, isn't it?'

'What's that got to do with you?'

'Don't be like that. I'm Norman Herbert. Don't you remember me? I was in the squad next to yours when we were at Inkermann Barracks in Woking in 1941. Look, don't sit there on your own. Come and join us, and meet my fiancée.'

I was surprised to find that the blonde at his table was an Italian, because blondes in Italy are a rarity.

During the next few weeks I saw a great deal of Norman. Naturally we went over all that happened to us since we had been drivers together. Gradually I learned the details of Norman's success story. It seems to me so fantastic as to be almost unbelievable had he not told it to me personally. I still see him and he lives in such splendour that it can be nothing but the truth.

After leaving O.C.T.U. at Boscombe near Bournemouth, Norman soon found himself in the Middle East. He was wounded in the Battle of Alamein when he ran his fifteen-hundredweight onto a mine. Luckily the floor was heavily packed with sandbags and he escaped with one leg shorter than the other. This made him decide that active warfare was not for him. He managed to get himself transferred to an insignificant job at GHQ, Cairo, where by doing absolutely nothing except send out reams and reams of bumpf, his war effort was much appreciated by his immediate superior. Between them they instigated a system of internal memos. They calculated that it took a whole week for one to circulate through the building and return duly initialled by various departments as having been read and contents noted, back to their desks.

Norman, however, unlike myself, was a man of initiative, a person who looked to the future. It seemed to him that it would be stupid of him to waste away his entire war, when it could without any harm to others, be turned to profitable use. It was while in Cairo that a casual remark dropped by one of the officers responsible for contracting fresh vegetables for the Eight Army, determined the path that he would take. This particular officer remarked to him one day at Groppis, 'The trouble with this bloody awful country is that there isn't one single honest Gippo amongst the whole bloody lot. Do you know, one of them had the impertinence to come to my office and offer me twenty per cent if I would give him a part of the water-melon contract?'

These words, or rather the three words twenty per cent made a great impression on Norman. You might say that they became indelibly written on his heart.

In due course he joined with the three divisions that comprised Allied Headquarters at Caserta Palace and it was there that he set about planning his future. By dint of arse-creeping, wire pulling and the aid of his natural charm and good looks, he managed to get himself transferred to a lowly position in a department responsible for contracting with the Italians for a certain fresh commodity. In the interests of security I cannot disclose which it was.

As I have mentioned earlier, if you were lucky enough to get yourself to Caserta, it was only a matter of time before you were promoted. As the officer above moved up one, everyone below followed him up in the game of Promotional Chairs. So in due course Norman found himself with the rank of Major in charge of a very handsome contract which was in his gift. Not being greedy, he farmed it out at the modest commission of fifteen per cent paid weekly in cash.

Many had got as far as this before Norman, and not a few had bungled it from here on and ended up behind bars. It was obviously no good stuffing the lovely lire into pillows; there was no way of transferring it back to the U.K. The only place to dispose of it was into an Italian Bank. Norman reckoned this was far from safe, as anyone with a contract like his was bound to be under surveillance by the security police.

Here luck came to Norman's aid. While he was on leave in Rome, while staying at the Grande he met and fell in love with the daughter of a famous Italian Industrialist, still thriving to this day. She was the blonde whom I had seen lunching with him at the Falstaff.

There was considerable opposition to the marriage from her parents, who rightly objected to their only daughter marrying a pauper in the Corps. But their only daughter was deeply in love with Norman and it was she who came up with the solution. Why not, she suggested, give her the money, and she would pay it into a Number Two Account at her bank? She would not touch it, and when the war was over there should be a handsome dowry for her and Papa could make no objection.

This is what Norman did. When the war ended he was a millionaire in lire several times over. When I met him he had recently transferred to a safe job in Naples. His wife, as now she was, wisely reasoned that he had made enough and it would be foolish to tempt fate and the police further for the sake of a few more lire.

Norman was demobilized at his own request in Italy soon after I met him and went back to live at his villa outside Florence.

Two years ago I happened to be visiting Florence and, not having seen him since 1946, I made enquiries as to where he lived.

The villa was magnificent. I regret to say that his beautiful blonde wife had turned into a rather dumpy uninteresting Italian matron. I was not surprised when I discovered that she had produced eight children. Norman confessed to me that he had not realized what a devout Catholic she was, and that she would follow the Pope's ruling on birth control to the last sperm.

On my happy visit to his villa Norman made one final confession. The magnificent villa had been a ruin when I met him in Naples, and at the time he was in the process of having it restored. As civilian transport was non-existent, he had been forced to use W.D. trucks. He had not told his wife because she thought he had washed his hands of all rackets and was frightened that he might get caught if he continued. But he had determined to bring his bride back to a villa suitable for her status and the great wealth of her family. Accordingly he had taken the risk without telling her or me, and paid a considerable sum of money to a company of the old Corps to transport the marble from the coast to Florence.

Strangely enough the company that did the work for him was one stationed at Salerno. It employed Italian drivers. It's boss man went by the name of Pietro.

To understand what follows I must point out that, although I may have given the impression that I had devoted my life in Naples to pleasure, drink and Maria, and had cut down my attendances at the German morning parade to one in three, I still toured the countryside looking at old dumps of ammunition and setting up new ones and I spent a considerable amount of time in the docks watching the ships unload their cargoes onto my trucks.

Security in the docks was still tight. It must have been the last place in Naples that there was any security left. Even so, rumours were going round the Officers' Club that a highly organized band of local robbers had managed to steal a Liberty ship bit by bit, and put it together at a smaller port further down the coast.

Every civilian employee in the docks was liable to be stripped and thoroughly searched on leaving. I myself had been taken into a small hut and made to strip down to my pants the second time I had gone there by an apologetic Lance-Corporal in the Security Police.

On the front of my Fordson Staff car was an impressive looking piece of paper. The kind of thing you see stuck on the front of the Rolls' and Bentleys as they trundle down the Mall to disgorge their occupants at a Royal Garden Party.

After a few weeks I had naturally become known to the Security Police, and there was no question of my being stopped, let alone of being searched. In other words I could come and go as I pleased, driven, of course, by my German Corporal.

I can remember the day well. It was August Bank Holiday, 1946. I had lunched with a crowd of officers I had met in the bar of the Officers' Club. We had talked nostalgically about England, and had laid bets as to whether it was raining in the U.K. or not. A signals officer had promised to put through a call to England to find out, and we had agreed to meet back at the Club around eight that evening to settle the bets.

Strangely enough as I made my way to the club off the Via Roma to continue drinking in the privacy of my box which was now reserved for my sole use, I was still moderately sober. I had determined to try to stay that way, and to take Maria on to a night club at Posillipo which had a magnificent view across the bay. Alternatively I could get my Corporal to drive us south along the coast road to Positano and we could spend a night dancing and drinking at the Buca di Bacco where the wine was at least drinkable and dry. Perhaps the reason for my sobriety was that I had heard a few days previously from one of the many acquaintances whom I met in the bar of the Officers' Club, who had the same demob number as myself, that he had heard a rumour that we were likely to be sent back to England any moment at short notice to be finally returned to civilian life. I had not paid a great deal of attention to this, as in the course of nearly five years in the army I had taught myself to expect the worst and to accept the best when it happened. This avoided disappointment.

I had sat down in the darkness of my box, having ordered a bottle of champagne, knowing that if I was to be sober by ten and take Maria out, whisky and brandy were out of the question. The usual tenor came on and cracked a few glasses, followed by Maria. As she sang one of the arias from Donizetti's *Elisir d'Amore*, I could not help thinking of Major Geoffrey Miller in whose company I had last seen it performed, and wondered how he was getting on in civilian life. It seemed unlikely that the Stock Exchange would supply him with the same amount of entertainment as he had found for the asking in Salerno and Naples. Being in that half state of drunkenness I felt maudlin, and the sight of bloated black marketeers and crooks, brought tears to my eyes. I was only too aware that I had used her like a proper shit, and then and there I determined to mend my ways and to treat her as a human being instead of an object.

Maria finished singing to a burst of applause and left the stage. I lay back in my chair waiting to hear the door behind me open and feel her soft hands round the back of my neck and hear her whisper: '*Come state caro mio?*' I heard the door open. Nothing further happened. Someone walked on to the stage and begun to belt out *O Sole Mio*.

I turned slowly in my chair. In the gloom of the box I could make out three figures standing with their backs to the wall. Behind them the door had been closed. I cannot explain why, but a great sense of unease descended upon me.

'Good afternoon, Capitano. I hope you are well and enjoying yourself,' one of them said.

'Who are you?'

'Surely you remember us? We came to your camp some six weeks back. Do you not remember me—Antonio?'

'Of course I do,' I said. 'What brings you here?'

The three figures remained in the darkness to the rear of the box. I turned my chair completely round so that I could face them. Unease had now been overtaken by fear.

'We need your help, Capitano. Don't worry. It is a very small thing that we will ask of you. There is no danger in it for you. First I must ask you one question. It is true, is it not, that you can go in and out of the docks as you please and that no one now thinks to stop the Capitano in his Fordson and put him through the shame of a search?'

'That is right.'

'Good, Capitano. Now you must ask no questions. It is better that way. What we would like you to do out of your friendship with Papa Pietro at Salerno is very simple. You will not go unrewarded, and of course all your expenses here and in the other clubs and restaurants of Naples will be taken care of'.

I sat in silence.

'You do not ask how much? When you have carried out this little job for us, your friends, we will arrange to pay forty thousand dollars into a bank in New York. After all, Italian money is of no use to you, and it is difficult for us to arrange it for you in England in pounds just at the moment.'

Still I said nothing.

'What you have to do is this, Capitano.' continued Antonio. 'In a few days a certain Liberty ship will dock at Naples. We do not wish to give you the name until she is safely alongside. It is not that we do not trust you, Capitano, but the fewer persons that know the better. All you have to do is this. We wish you to board her as soon as she has been cleared by your security men. There is no difficulty about that, is there?'

'No,' I said. 'There is no difficulty.'

I often boarded the ships that my Germans were unloading to have a drink with the Captain or other members of the crew. Sometimes I would come ashore with a crate of whisky and gin, provided of course that it was a British ship as the American ones were mostly dry.

'Good. You will go aboard this ship where you will be met by one of the officers. You will point out your Fordson car to him. Nothing more. You will then have a drink with him on the ship, and he will soon say good-bye to you. All you have to do then is to walk off the ship, get into your Fordson car, and tell your German Corporal to bring you here. When you arrive here you will send the German Corporal round to the kitchen for a meal, which you have done before. He now knows that the car is safe under the eyes of the men on the door and he will not mind leaving it. That is all you have to do, Capitano. It is not too much that your friends are asking, is it, Capitano?'

'No.'

'Good. It has been a pleasure to meet you again, and I will not keep you from your delightful Maria. She is a good girl, is she not? Have no fear about the dollars. We will see to your expenses in Naples. We are men of our word, Capitano.' Here Antonio paused. 'We expect our friends to be men of their word too, Capitano.'

Antonio inclined his head towards me.

The next moment I was alone in the box.

I had started by feeling uneasy. Unease had turned to fear, fear to terror.

I was under no illusion as to what I was being asked to bring out of the docks in my Fordson staff car. Drugs. I was not sure which drug, probably heroin or cocaine. Possibly opium for processing in Naples, which was already rivalling Marseilles as the centre for refining the raw materials. I had heard about the sudden rise in the drug traffic in the bars and clubs of Naples, and also in the Officers' Club. There had been an acute shortage of drugs of all kinds in Italy as a result of the war, and by now they were taking over from rubber as the most valuable commodity on the black market. Drugs took up little space and were easy to handle, and the rewards were colossal. Why else should Antonio and his gang be prepared to pay me the sum of forty thousand dollars for taking my car into the docks, having a drink aboard a Liberty ship and driving out again?

It seemed to me that there were only three options open to me, as I sat in the box that late afternoon and tried to sort out the problem. I could go ahead as requested and collect forty thousand dollars, with the chance of being caught and facing a heavy sentence in goal. I could decline the task Antonio had set me, in which case I hadn't the slightest doubt he would go to the Military Authorities and complain about my debts which now amounted to nearly three thousand pounds. That was the least he would do. He would probably inform them that I had been implicated in some shady deals while with the Italian Civilian Company at Salerno. I didn't doubt for one minute that he would be able to produce all the witnesses in the world to testify against me. Finally I could go to the Security Police and make a clean breast of the whole affair. But policemen are funny people. There was no guarantee that I would be granted complete immunity. Certainly I would be detained in Italy for months while enquiries were made. If the affair came to court I could see myself in Italy for a year or more.

Five minutes after I had been left alone in the box, Maria joined me. I do not know how much she knew. Certainly she sensed that something was very wrong. She was kinder and more gentle with me than I had ever imagined possible. Looking back I think she must have been aware of the mess in which I had landed myself.

We never went to Posilippo, let alone Positano, that night.

Ten minutes after she came into the box I ordered a bottle of Scotch. I didn't even spend the night at her place because, before she came off stage at ten o'clock, I had staggered out of the club and my German Corporal had taken me back to the camp where I must have been put to bed by some of my former enemies. For the next morning I woke up in my hut wearing pyjamas, which I could not possibly have succeeded in putting on by myself.

All the following day I went over the situation step by step, posing questions, giving answers, but always coming back to the three options open to me.

In order to try to clear my head I determined not to drink, but by midday I felt so shaky that I drank several glasses of white Frascati. At least it steadied my hands so that they ceased to shake.

By one o'clock I had come to the conclusion that until I had made up my mind what to do, I must carry on as usual. I was tempted to stay in the camp where I would be well protected by members of the Wehrmacht. But I couldn't stay there forever. At some point or other I must show my face at the docks or the Officers' Club or even at Headquarters which I visited now and again, or questions might be raised as to my whereabouts.

I was about to send a runner to tell my Corporal to bring the car round to take me to the Officers' Club when there was a knock at the door. My nerves must have been in a very poor state because I jumped in the air. I opened the door.

One of the Germans was outside. He held out a buff-coloured envelope. 'For you, Herr Hauptmann.'

I tore it open, not particularly caring what was inside. It was bound to be some damn fool request from Headquarters. Possibly a couple of rounds of twenty-five pounder shells were unaccounted for.

Does the devil look after his own? He certainly did that summer afternoon in Naples, 1946.

It was a movement order instructing me to report forthwith to Rome Airport to be flown to the U.K. where I would be demobilized on arrival at Aldershot. Corporal Robertson would take over charge of the Company until such time as another officer would be appointed.

I literally ran to Corporal Robertson's hut. I had not seen him for several days. With shaking hands I held the order under his nose.

All he said was, 'I think it's best you got away right now, Sirr.' I did not at the time consider the significance of his remark. Later on, back in England, I wondered how much he knew.

Within two hours I was in the Fordson staff car speeding north to Rome. I didn't stay in the Grande. I felt safer in the transit camp near to the airport even if the food was disgusting and the bed hard. At four o'clock the following morning I set foot in the U.K.

I am ashamed to say I never said good-bye to Maria. I hope she eventually escaped from the clutches of the Mafia, although I very much doubt it.

Although I have been back to Italy several times since the war, I must confess that to begin with it was with a feeling of nervousness. I'm told that the arm and the memory of the Mafia is long.

I have never visited Naples since that day although it is to me one of the most beautiful cities in the world.

As I write this nearly thirty years after that day I returned to England, I can honestly say that had I been able to forsee the disasters, miseries, and failures, that lay lurking in wait for me in civvy street, I would have signed on as a Regular Soldier in the Army.

But I doubt very much if the Army would have accepted the offer of my services.